2009

Little Laureates

Edited by Lisa Adlam

First published in Great Britain in 2010 by

 Young**Writers**

Remus House
Coltsfoot Drive
Peterborough
PE2 9JX
Telephone: 01733 890066
Website: www.youngwriters.co.uk

Foreword

At Young Writers our defining aim is to promote an enjoyment of reading and writing amongst children and young adults. By giving aspiring poets the opportunity to see their work in print, their love of the written word as well as confidence in their own abilities has the chance to blossom.

Our latest competition Poetry Explorers was designed to introduce primary school children to the wonders of creative expression. They were given free reign to write on any theme and in any style, thus encouraging them to use and explore a variety of different poetic forms.

We are proud to present the resulting collection of regional anthologies which are an excellent showcase of young writing talent. With such a diverse range of entries received, the selection process was difficult yet very rewarding. From comical rhymes to poignant verses, there is plenty to entertain and inspire within these pages. We hope you agree that this collection bursting with imagination is one to treasure.

Contents

Roseberry Primary School, Billingham

Swinderby All Saints Primary School, Lincoln

Thurston CE (VC) Primary School, Bury St Edmunds

The Poems

My Tick-Tock Clock

Tick-tock, tick-tock,
It's the clock,
Round and square,
It's always there.

Roman numbers
All the way round,
Only one hand
Makes a sound.
Not too big,
Not too tiny,
But with the colour black,
It makes it shiny.

When I'm asleep,
The clock makes a loud sound,
This makes my eyes go right round,
I see the clock,
Oh no! It's past nine o'clock!
I am shocked,
'Mum! Dad! It's past nine o'clock!'
'Don't be silly, it's only seven o'clock!'

I come back from school
And see the clock
It still goes tick-tock.

Ishika Haque (11)

Pyramids

P yramids - some gold at the top, some not gold at the top
Y eek! Scary
R agged steps on some pyramids, no ragged steps on others
A ncient pharaohs
M ummified
I am scared
D isgusting
S laves worked to build them.

Tom Garnier (8)

1

Treasure

A spark so great hit my eye
Then I let out a very shocked cry,
Colours everywhere made me blind..
I looked side to side, in front and behind
Colours everywhere making me blind
Golds, silvers, blues and greens,
I could load a sack full
But the colours would break the seams.
I picked a great big chunk of blue
It wasn't as heavy as my shoe,
In fact I could throw it to Timbucktoo.
I walked out of the cave into the light,
Still gripping my chunk of blue very tight,
I walked and walked to the top of the hill,
Where lived a wise wizard who lived in the mill.
He was ancient, wise, clever and old,
His robes were the colours of silver and gold.
I knocked on the door
And kneeled on the floor,
Out he came,
I must've looked lame,
But he smiled and leaned on his knobbly cane
And said, 'Tell me your story of your new glory.'
So I told him my story which contained all my glory,
Then the wizard said . . .
'It gives me great pleasure
To say that you are the first person
To find something called treasure.'

Anna Geaney (10)
Amberfield School, Ipswich

My Dog And Me

I was walking my dog in the dark
When suddenly she began to bark
I turned and saw
What she was barking for
She had seen a light in the wood
And started running as fast as she could
I was left alone in the night
The sound of wolves gave me a fright
So I followed my dog
But tripped over a log
And fell in a bog
I yelled for help
My dog gave a yelp
As she came to my aid
With a rope she had made
She pulled and she pulled
She pulled and she pulled
Till I was unstuck
Covered in muck
I called Mum on my phone
And said we would shortly be home
I was glad to be free
And ran home for my tea
Full of glee
My dog and me.

Natalie Wills (11)
Amberfield School, Ipswich

3

My Mum

My mum, she's a magical magician.
A dream that has just come true.
But she is a dream away.
She is over the mountains, under a tunnel, past all the rivers.
She is in Olympus
Where she shall rest forever with the gods and goddesses.
She is a dream.
She is like a star shining in the night sky
With a beam, such a beam that you could dream,
Dream your day away.
She's a drama queen, a brilliant actress
Like my teacher Mrs Dungey.
She can fly like a bird soaring,
Just soaring like a bird.
She is my mum, no one could be as
Loving or caring as my mum.
She's killed evil witches, she's fought brave sorcerers,
She has saved the world.
No one, no, no one can be as brave,
Loving, caring or cunning as my mum.

Molly Willis (10)
Amberfield School, Ipswich

A Snowy Sunday

Swirling snow all around
Sounds of crunching on the ground,
Mum, Dad, Xander, Liv and me,
Throwing snowballs till it's time for tea.
Icy and wet, we go inside,
'I am freezing cold' I cried
I ripped off my clothes and snuggled by the fire,
Hot chocolate with cream my only desire,
Playing games in the firelight,
Our shadows flicker, it's a homely sight.

Florence Haywood-Smith (10)
Amberfield School, Ipswich

My Family

My family is something you can't buy,
You cannot take it,
You cannot lie.
My family is something strange,
For my father is an astronaut
Who travels through the solar system.
He has seen every star,
Although he hasn't got very far.
Now let's see about Mother,
Well, she's a movie star.
No one is quite like her,
She is mighty fine,
No one has a mother like mine,
I don't worry about my brother,
He's a little horror,
Oh, fancy that!
I forgot about my cats.
There's not another girl like me,
And there never will be!

Eleanor Roberts (10)
Amberfield School, Ipswich

A Cat Named Pickle

Pickle is a fluffy cat,
She has a fuzzy tail,
Her eyes are big and brown,
Pickle has sharp claws that dig into the ground
There are paw marks everywhere.
She will gobble up her food.
Then have a long nap.
Pickle is a naughty cat,
She will climb all different types of trees,
She will chase the dog any place, even round the trees.

Freya Morris (11)
Amberfield School, Ipswich

The Bet

The ball came at me, I had to be tough,
If I smash it down the line will that be enough?
To win me the point and maybe the set,
Or even the match, then I'll win my bet.

Nobody thinks I can beat this seed
The number one from Herts,
A player that's no weed.
But I have a plan that will take her out fast
If my serve works, she won't stand a chance.
I'll go corner to corner
And then down the line,
A nice little drop-shot to finish this time,
Then my bet is won,
My day of sheer bliss,
My mummy will hate it,
She'll tear out her hair,
And what is this bet, this promise so fair?
Why, a whole day of choosing in Build-a-Bear!

Nia Braidford (10)
Amberfield School, Ipswich

Ruby's Walk

Rattle the lead and she comes running!
Hoping that I will say those words,
'Are you coming?' I finally say,
In those words excitement grows.
She jumps around and runs to the door,
I struggle to put the lead on her.
Finally we're ready to go!
She races me to the door,
Off we go, Ruby.

Rose Power (10)
Amberfield School, Ipswich

My Dad

My dad's not brilliant,
My dad's okay,
My dad's sort of weird,
But in his own special way.

He doesn't play much sport,
He doesn't build or mend,
He doesn't write many letters,
And emails he never sends.

He doesn't wipe the tables,
Or do the laundry,
He can't remember his passwords,
Or where he leaves his keys.

My dad's sometimes crazy,
Sometimes he's mad as hatters,
But my dad loves me,
And that's all that matters.

Elizabeth Jones (10)
Amberfield School, Ipswich

My Little Puppy Ruby

I've always wanted a puppy,
A puppy of my own,
And now I have my Ruby,
We have given her a home.

Ruby is so cute,
Ruby is so sweet,
Ruby is always at my feet.

She loves to play in the garden,
She loves to play all day,
Ruby is my puppy,
She's my number one!

Isobella Rivers (10)
Amberfield School, Ipswich

In The Bath

In the bath my sister goes
As happy as can be
And when she touches the water
She splashes frantically
When you hear her laugh
It will fill you with glee
But if she grows up
Where will my baby be?
Maybe she'll be like
A fish diving in the sea
Who likes to have
Adventures along with me
In the big blue sea
But I don't have to worry
Because she's only a baby
And I'll just have to see.

Hollie Harrell (11)
Amberfield School, Ipswich

The Pickpocket

I crept up behind him, and slipped my hand in,
And took out a wallet, which was just within,
I ran as fast as I could and hid behind a wall,
Hoping no one had seen me, no one at all,
I crept down dark alleyways and down winding streets,
'Til I got to the place, where my gang always meets,
I looked around the building, but no one was there,
And then I heard footsteps, behind me somewhere,
Then suddenly with no warning, through the door of our den,
Came two quickly descending village policemen,
They captured me hurriedly before I could react,
And swiftly tied my hands behind my back,
Then rather unkindly, thumped me on the head,
And that's when I woke up screaming in bed!

Amelia Williams (10)
Amberfield School, Ipswich

The Island

I land on an island
And bump my head
Someone drags me here and there
I see a cave
He throws me in there
I hear a noise
That scares me in there
I run out and climb a tree
And I see a hungry bear that growls at me
He climbs the tree
I am at the end
And I jump off the tree
He flies in the air into the water
He cries and cries
He can't swim
I walk and find a key
That means I'm on a treasure hunt
I look for clues from side to side
I bump my head on a rock
I find a map
What does it say?
Ten feet that way and again and again
I get cross
So I have a break
It's turned dark
So I sleep there
I wake up and find a box
It has a lock
The shape of a key
And I open it and find gold!

Aparna Kalhan (8)
Beehive Preparatory School, Ilford

My Treasure

I explore an island,
What will I find?
Will I find buried treasure.
Or emeralds and rubies?
I will travel on a boat.
Beat every pirate.
I shall destroy any animal
That dares to fight me.
I will search
Until I find my treasure, never stop!
I will go through thick and thin
Never give up
I will go past caves, seas, countries,
And my heart.
Then I might get hungry,
Need food, need food,
Can't stop.
What a stroke of luck,
Need to eat that food.
Continue searching
Find a map.
Dusty it is.
Getting dark.
How about some sleep?
24 hours gone
Back to finding my treasure.
Okay, I have to get past the rocks first.
Now I've found the rocks.
They are sharp.
How do I get past these rocks?
Ah-ha a vine.
Now I just need
To use this to get across the rocks
I did it!
Next I need to get past the river.
A boat, good.
Now to get past the river.

Past the river.
Good, now to get past the cave.
In the cave.
I'm out.
Now to my treasure.
There is my treasure.
A key.
Now to open it.
Gold!

Arbaab Anwar (8)
Beehive Preparatory School, Ilford

My Magical Carpet

My magic carpet
Takes me everywhere
And sometimes places
Which are unknown
Beyond this world
It takes me
With cowboys, dragons,
Monsters and even dragonflies
But today I came to a castle
With rats and bats flying
And things crawling here and there
I found some gold
Which was precious
Then there was a falcon
Which was a little bit scary
And I think it looked a little bit hairy
I asked my carpet to get me away
And it did what I did say
But I didn't get any treasure
In my magic carpet adventures
I will try again
To get some precious treasure.

Apisan Easwarathasan (8)
Beehive Preparatory School, Ilford

Deep Under The Sea

There I was 60 feet under the sea,
Looking for the white sea stingray.
It was big and shy
But still lived under the sea.
Nobody knew if it was a female or male.
Then I bumped into someone.
Who could it be under the sea?
It was a girl looking
For the white sea stingray
Then I heard a roar
Under the deep sea
The girl and I decided to go
Deep under the sea
Then I felt something tickling my feet.
Deep under the sea.
I looked down, I saw the white sea stingray.
It glared at me
And swam away
I hoped I could see it
Another day.
As I swam to shore I said, 'At least I saw a white stingray.'

Khush Patel (8)
Beehive Preparatory School, Ilford

Down I Go

Down I go, down I go,
To the bottom of the cellar
It gets darker and darker
Here I go.
Here I find spiders' webs and lots of dust.
There's a chest full of old toys,
Down I go, down I go
Here I am.
Here I am at the bottom of the cellar
Dust gets on my clothes as I go.
Now I'm down.
Now I'm down.
I have to go up again,
Up I go, up I go.
Spider's web
And lots of toys in my hand.
Up I go
Here I am up.
I am in the house again.
I am up
In the light again.

Sayali Chauhan (8)
Beehive Preparatory School, Ilford

Hidden Hats

I found some hidden treasure
Deep down in the sea.
I tried to open it up
But it would not open for me.
I tried to find the key
But it was no use.
Then I heard a sparkling noise
Under a shoe.
I followed its sound,
It was getting close
And I found it
But it dropped on a stone.
I couldn't go down it because
It was too dark for me.
I had to go down.
I got the key
Then I went back.
I went to open it
But it was only a box of hats.

Judy Zoradey (8)
Beehive Preparatory School, Ilford

I'm A Little Explorer

I'm a little explorer
Who searches for gold,
Island to island.
Watch how I go.
I dig up hidden treasure
But all I find is wood.
I search high above
And search down low.
But I cannot find anything
So off I go.

Tulsi Patel (8)
Beehive Preparatory School, Ilford

Discovery Of The Lion

I was walking in the jungle
And I discovered a lion.
I discovered a lion
So I screamed
For my mum
But she didn't come.
The lion was ready
To gobble me up
Any second.
I screamed
And I screamed
And it was just standing there.
I looked behind me
And I saw a lot of lions.
They all got into a circle
And I heard a voice saying,
April fool!

Mahnoor Malik (8)
Beehive Preparatory School, Ilford

I Explore The Desert

I am an explorer in the desert
It's my favourite thing
I look everywhere
I sleep in pyramids
I've seen the Valley of Kings
I've seen the Valley of Queens
I've seen mummies
I've seen lots of creatures
There's lots of danger
I sometimes find caves
I look for gold
I am an explorer in the desert
The desert is amazing!

Nafeesa Aziz (8)
Beehive Preparatory School, Ilford

The Dragon Who Was On fire

There was an explorer
Who journeyed into the forest
Searching for gold.
He got lost.
He was digging in the forest
When he spotted something gold.
He picked it up.
He found it was plastic
So he dropped it.
He was digging till dawn.
He saw a cave
That he could sleep in.
What he didn't know was
It was a dragon's cave.
So when he reached it,
He had to fight a 20 foot dragon.
How he did it goes like this:
He got some wood and forced the dragon to put it on fire
And then he set the dragon on fire!

Himanshu Singh (7)
Beehive Preparatory School, Ilford

My Name's Pat

My name is Pat
I like to go on adventures
And discover new things.
When I grow up I'm going to
Explore the world.
In deserts, islands
Jungles and other places.
Everyone in our
Family knows I like adventures,
Mum says I'm too small to go,
so I look in our basement.
My name's Pat, I love cats and other animals
But I don't like snakes, *eugh!*
Next week it's my birthday, I'm going to be ten
Then I'm going to looks for hens
My name is Pat, I love to explore and explore and explore.
Mum thinks I'll get lost anywhere
But I'll live with funny bears.
My name's Pat and I love to explore.

Savera Hussain (9)
Beehive Preparatory School, Ilford

Pretend Secret

I live in a secret countryside
Which no one knows about.
It has a hill of snowdrops,
And a magic stream,
It has grass which shines in the sun
From rain which fell softly as the wind blew a breeze,
But one thing may surprise you, though I know this place well,
I only know this part.
And so I decided to explore.
I took food and drink and helpful supplies,
I went round the hill and across the stream
To find a door in the middle of nowhere.
I found a city.
It was all an adventure in my secret countryside.
A giant came and she gave me a bath
Before a lovely hot dinner.
Then she read me a scroll of a message from my friend.
A made-up explorer.

Umama Uddin (8)

Beehive Preparatory School, Ilford

Diamond Explorer

I'm an explorer,
I search for diamonds
Inside the rocky mountains.
I read a big signpost which said *No Mining*.
I ignored it.
I started bashing the rocks.
Suddenly the rocks fell down the mountain.
I was a little frightened
And I started bashing rocks again.
Finally I found a diamond.
Suddenly I heard a big thud
And saw a rock
The size of a double-decker bus.
I screamed
As the rock smashed me on the head.
I fell down and fainted.
When I woke up
I said, 'I am never going exploring again!'

Nikhil Purohit (8)
Beehive Preparatory School, Ilford

Can I Be An Explorer?

I want to be an explorer
Find everything outside
Look for creatures or animals
Or find some pieces of gold
Lots of things that I haven't seen
Maybe some real life dinosaurs
Or dragons in the wild
I can find some diamonds
Or little jewels
Why can't everyone be an explorer?
For exploring is so much fun
Lots of people can discover things
And live a happy life
I could be an explorer
If I grow up fast.

Jathavi Thirukumaran (8)
Beehive Preparatory School, Ilford

The Diamond Lamb

I'm an exploring tiger.
I'm full of fear and disgrace.
I eat toads, frogs, elephants and people.
I eat my prey every day.
My mission is to find the diamond lamb.
I have twenty meals a day.
I dream of eating meat all day
Then I saw a shiny lamb.
I said, '*Hip hip hooray.*'
Then I found it was a mirror shining
With a sticker which looked like a lamb
I cried and cried.
I fell on a button
Then the diamond lamb was found.

Davin Bacheta (8)
Beehive Preparatory School, Ilford

The Explorer

I went exploring
I never ever gave up
I looked at my map for hidden treasure
I saw scary animals
I climbed up the mountain
I searched there
I found a golden coin
I saw a big amazing tiger
I got scared
I ran up the mountain
I came back down
The tiger ran away
Then I saw the magic carpet come to take me back home.

Serina Khilochia (8)
Beehive Preparatory School, Ilford

Angry Is . . .

Angry is . . .
The colour red.
The smell of fighting.
The sound of roaring.
The taste of blood.
The sight of wasted sweeties.
The feel of Mum waking me up for school.

Zander Heneghan (7)
Brora Primary School, Brora

Scared Is . . .

Scared is . . .
The colour of yellow
The smell of fire
The sound of footsteps
The taste of poisoned berries
The sight of a ghost
The feel of a big dog.

Hannah Wilson (7)
Brora Primary School, Brora

Terrified Is . . .

Terrified is . . .
The colour of black
The smell of a monster
The sound of scratching
The taste of blood
The sight of someone in the dark
The feel of snake's skin.

Leah Simpson (7)
Brora Primary School, Brora

Scared Is . . .

Scared is . . .
The colour of black.
The smell of fire.
The sound of bombs.
The taste of blood.
The sight of a ghost.
The feel of goo.

Layton MacLeod (8)
Brora Primary School, Brora

Surprise Is . . .

Surprise is . . .
The colour of bright pink.
The smell of cakes cooking.
The sound of a puppy.
The taste of chocolate.
The sight of a funfair.
The feel of a puppy's fur.

Ellie Fox (7)
Brora Primary School, Brora

Fun Is . . .

Fun is . . .
The colour of yellow.
The smell of candyfloss.
The sound of music.
The taste of hotdogs.
The sight of flashing lights.
The feel of fluffiness.

Annaleigh Breau (7)
Brora Primary School, Brora

Surprise Is . . .

Surprise is . . .
The colour of bright pink.
The smell of cakes cooking.
The sound of a party.
The taste of sour lemons.
The sight of a funfair.
The feel of a puppy.

Connie Taylor (7)
Brora Primary School, Brora

Sadness

Sadness smells like eggs.
Sadness feels like hot coal.
Sadness looks like a stabbed man.
Sadness tastes like kidney beans.
Sadness sounds like a screaming baby.
Sadness is the colour of dark grey.
Sadness reminds me of hitting my head on ice.

Struan Johnstone (11)
Brora Primary School, Brora

Happiness

Happiness smells like chocolate.
Happiness feels like chocolate melting.
Happiness looks like play parks.
Happiness tastes like cookies.
Happiness sounds like birds singing.
Happiness reminds me of winning a trophy.
Happiness is the colour of blue.

Robbie Urquhart (10)
Brora Primary School, Brora

Love

Love smells like the morning red roses.
Love feels like the morning air.
Love looks like roses and hearts.
Love tastes like home-made jam doughnuts.
Love sounds like the ringing of a Valentine's card.
Love is the colour of red and pink.
Love reminds me of happy people and hearts and roses.

Caitlin Campbell (10)
Brora Primary School, Brora

Happiness

Happiness is the smell of fairy cakes.
Happiness is the feel of a fluffy pillow.
Happiness is the sight of birds.
Happiness is the taste of chocolate.
Happiness is the sound of laughter.
Happiness is the colour of yellow and light pink.
It reminds me of a sunny day.

Demi Payne (10)
Brora Primary School, Brora

Happiness

Happiness feels like I just want to jump with joy.
Happiness smells like freshly baked cake.
Happiness looks like chocolate cake.
Happiness tastes like hot chocolate.
Happiness sounds like the sound of my Wii.
Happiness is the colour of yellow.
Happiness reminds me of Club Penguin.

Lewis MacLennan (11)
Brora Primary School, Brora

Happiness

Happiness smells like rosy apples.
Happiness feels like chocolate melting in your hands.
Happiness looks like daisies blooming.
Happiness tastes like sherbet exploding in your mouth.
Happiness sounds like birds calling.
Happiness is the colour of yellow.
Happiness reminds me of summer days.

Jeannie Urquhart (11)
Brora Primary School, Brora

Silence

Silence smells like cold wind
Silence feels like you're alone
Silence looks like empty space
Silence tastes like bitter chocolate
Silence sounds like no one's there
Silence is the colour of grey
Silence reminds me of sadness.

Eva Scott (10)
Brora Primary School, Brora

Happiness

Happiness is the smell of chocolate.
Happiness is the feel of a cat's smooth, fluffy coat.
Happiness is the look of smiley faces.
Happiness is the taste of great food.
Happiness is the sound of cheers from everyone.
Happiness is the colour of the bright yellow sunshine.
Happiness reminds me of a great family holiday.

Ryan MacKenzie (11)
Brora Primary School, Brora

Happiness

Happiness smells like sweet honey.
Happiness feels like bouncing on my trampoline.
Happiness looks like dazzling stars.
Happiness tastes like freshly baked cakes.
Happiness sounds like a cry of laughter.
Happiness is the colour of sunshine yellow.
Happiness reminds me of enjoying myself.

Joanna MacLean (9)
Brora Primary School, Brora

Happiness

Happiness is the smell of cakes baking.
Happiness is the feel of sand between your toes.
Happiness is the sight of shining stars.
Happiness is the taste of good food.
Happiness is the sound of birds.
Happiness is the colour of love.

George Gunn (11)
Brora Primary School, Brora

Gleaming Stars

Rapidly gleaming atop the night sky,
Brighter and brighter the star flashes by
One million miles from the spot where I stand
Stardust that's made of ice, rock and sand.
It illuminates the sky I am watching above,
And transforms into the shape of a gleaming white dove.
The star I am watching it glows in the night,
And believe me when I say it's a dazzling sight.
It won't last forever, it will soon leave my vision,
But for now it moves with grace and precision.
Beside it stands a constellation of three,
'Orion's Belt!' I realise now that's something to see.
As it begins to leave my eyesight,
I close my eyes and close them tight.
When I open them the star is nowhere in sight.
It's blinding brightness now a shimmering light.
Now it is gone the star so dazzling to see,
But now someone else can appreciate it just like me.
All around the world people can see
The star that is so special to me.
It won't last forever, it'll soon disappear
And as I watch it go I shed a small tear.
All around the world people can see,
The star that I love and the star that loves me.

Alistair Crooks (10)
Burgh School, Galashiels

Fairies Aren't So Nice!

Fairies aren't so nice,
They'll boil you and turn you into rice!
If you don't want to be a curry,
Then run in a hurry
'Cause fairies aren't so nice!

They'll put a curse on you,
Or turn you into stew!
But fairies are bad,
They'll make you feel sad
'Cause fairies aren't so nice!

Fairies live underground,
They don't like to be found.
So if you do,
Kick of your shoes
And run like the wind!

Fairies are best friends with trolls,
Or maybe half-humans, half-foals.
So don't insult a fairy,
'Cause you'll start to grow weary
And then you'll be hypnotised!

Fairies aren't so nice,
They'll boil you and turn you into rice!
If you don't want to be a curry,
Then run in a hurry
'Cause fairies aren't so nice!

Ryan Cheyne (10)
Burgh School, Galashiels

28

What An Extraordinary Day

The delicate cloud is floating in the indigo sky.
A murky mist is making the sky go incredibly dull.
The gloomy haze is fading softly away with the blustery wind.
Now the sky has gone back to its usual enchanting indigo colour.
Everyone's delighted to have had such a marvellous day.

Busy bees are buzzing in the charming sky.
Robins and bluetits are cheerful in song.
Ladybirds are lovingly fluttering around.
Butterflies are resting on brightly coloured buttercups.
Everything's peaceful and kind,
Everyone's delighted to have had such a marvellous day.

The scorching hot sun is setting gradually over the horizon.
All games are ending but everyone's had their fun.
The stars are shining high above the chimney tops and the
happiness of the children.
Everyone's tired but can't wait for the fun to start again tomorrow.
Everyone's delighted to have had such a marvellous day.

Lauren Thomson (9)
Burgh School, Galashiels

I'm An Academic Alien

I come from Mars
I have 3 heads
And I love Mars bars.

I have 19 eyes
And 7 wiggly toes
3 small bony arms
And a long green nose.

I have a spaceship
That I love to fly
I'm now off to Neptune
So adios, goodbye.

Liam Shillinglaw (10)
Burgh School, Galashiels

What I Saw

I saw a cotton candy cloud
Floating in the sky
I also saw some sherbet sand
And then I waved goodbye.

The trees turned into broccoli
The grass turned into chives
Everything turned into food
Except all the beehives.

Then it started raining
Raining popcorn that was sweet
I also started eating it
I thought it was rather neat.

People turned into gummy bears
We used jelly to draw
I have no idea what happened
But that is what I saw!

Keira Sutherland (9)
Burgh School, Galashiels

Ma Wee Scottish Moose

I yince had a moose
A wee, wee moose
That ran and ran round ma hoose.
Soft un furry
And aye in a hurry.

That wee, wee moose
That ran and ran roond ma hoose.

Until yin day ma big, fat cat
Decided that he'd have ma moose
And that was that.

That wee, wee moose
That ran and ran roond ma hoose.

So that was the end o' ma wee moose.
That yiste run and run roond ma hoose.

Euan Brown (10)
Burgh School, Galashiels

A Scottish Morning

As usual the morning brings a dreary tedious morning
The trees, the world, everything sopping, damp
A typical Scottish morning is dawning
Stretching across, I eagerly turn on the lamp.

Slowly and tiredly I hesitantly throw on my clothes
I stagger and stumble then I stand tall
I start to feel proud because everyone knows
That Scotland is a vision which is stunning to all!

To wander across the hills so high
The views, the lochs, the boats at sea
Lying below looking at the red sky
Scotland's my home, the best place for *me!*

Steven Patterson (10)
Burgh School, Galashiels

The Night Sky

See a star from afar up in the sky, like a giant firefly.
So blinding and shiny, elegantly illuminating the night sky.
The night sky getting lighter and lighter.
All around the world faster and faster.

Now it's a glorious morning you may not see them there
The stars high above, under the blanket without a care
Under the sun's light, you won't believe the sight
Like a blazing fireball all day and night.

I get in a fight feeling angry and upset
But I know what to do, to feel better I bet
And I lie on a hill and look at the constellation
And inside I get a warm sensation.

Fraser Drysdale (10)
Burgh School, Galashiels

Rainforest!

R ainforests can be found all around the world next to the warm
   equator
A nd they have lots of different animals and plants.
I n the rainforest there are four different colourful layers.
N oises in the rainforest can be extraordinarily loud and sometimes
   quiet.
F lowers from the rainforest are made into medicine.
O pen spaces in some places because trees are getting cut down
   to make wood.
R ainforest animals are dying because of this.
E normous animals live in the rainforest and some little animals.
S un shines in the emergent layer, canopy layer, understory layer
   but doesn't quite reach the forest floor.
T ribes are people who live in the rainforest and make fires to keep
   themselves warm.

Marisha Rygielski (11)
Cochrane Castle Primary School, Johnstone

Rainforest

R ainforests can be found in different parts all around the world.
A nd lots of unexpected animals live there.
I n the rainforest there are four different layers with lots of species of animals and snails.
N ature is all around in the rainforest.
F antastic things go on in the rainforest like giving birth to baby animals.
O xygen is in the rainforest to keep the animals alive.
R ain keeps the animals alive because they need water and all through the year it rains over 200 feet.
E verything seems very open in some spaces.
S nails, snakes and spiders live in the four layers.
T he rainforest is dying out because people are cutting down trees and so they need to stop!

Chandler Harper (11)
Cochrane Castle Primary School, Johnstone

The Rainforest

R ainforests are scary, dark and crawling with insects.
A ll different animals live in the rainforest, some dangerous, some not.
I ntelligence comes from the rainforest - they make things that we still use today.
N ature is getting killed as well as animals.
F ascinating things come from the rainforest and the rainforest itself is fascinating.
O pen variety comes from the rainforest, it helps us with oxygen.
R ats and interesting nature: Flowers, oranges, rabbits, elephants, snakes and trees.
E normous animals run riot around the rainforest.
S un is very important because it helps the trees grow.
T ribes live in the rainforest, they provide lots of helpful things.

Stuart Hillon (10)
Cochrane Castle Primary School, Johnstone

The Rainforest

R ainforests can be found around the world
A nd all the animals and flowers can be found in different layers.
I n the emergent layer there are over 2000 different butterflies.
N ature is made in the rainforest for the animals.
F orest flowers make up at least two-thirds of the world's species of plants.
O ak trees are most found next to the warm equator.
R ainforests need rain of up to 2 metres yearly.
E xtraordinary animals are in the rainforest like the sloths and lungfish.
S nakes are dangerous with the venom they hold, just like the anaconda.
T ribes are the people that stay in the huts in the forest.

Declan Lilley (11)
Cochrane Castle Primary School, Johnstone

The Rainforest

R ainforests can be found in Madagascar and South America.
A ll sorts of animals can be found in the rainforest.
I n many rainforests the moisture remains high all year.
N ature is all around the rainforests.
F orests of South East Asia where the monsoon brings sudden high levels of rain
O ver half of the world's rainforests are found in South America.
R ainforests are found around the world in areas near the
E quator.
S outh America has the biggest rainforest in the world.
T he rainforests are sometimes called equatorial rainforests.

Liam Duffy (11)
Cochrane Castle Primary School, Johnstone

Rainforest

R ainforests have lots of trees.
A nd it is big and scary.
I t has lots of animals and scary noises.
N early nobody goes in the rainforest.
F rogs are jumping around.
O ranges are hanging from the trees.
R abbits are bouncing around the forest floor.
E lephants are making loud noises with their feet.
S piders make their webs on trees.
T rees can be very big in the rainforest.

Robert Carter (10)
Cochrane Castle Primary School, Johnstone

Rainforest

R ain falls rapidly among the layers.
A ll different animals live in the rainforest.
I nteresting facts have been found out by scientists.
N ectar is a sweet liquid produced by many flowers.
F ruit bats are large bats that eat fruit and flowers.
O rang-utans are large, tree swinging apes.
R ed bellied piranhas are meat eating, freshwater fish.
E lephants are big, tall animals with long trunks.
S ome people live in the rainforest, they're called tribes.
T ribes are a group of people who live in huts.

Kayleigh Waters (11)
Cochrane Castle Primary School, Johnstone

The Rainforest

R ainforests have four layers.
A ll layers have animals living in them.
I nsects live in the trees in the rainforest.
N oises come from the rainforest.
F lowers and plants live in the rainforest.
O pen spaces are around in places.
R ainforests have 2 metres worth of rain every week.
E lephants live in the rainforest.
S un travels through the rainforest.
T he tropical rainforest is what we are studying.

Jonathan McDougall (11)
Cochrane Castle Primary School, Johnstone

Rainforest

R ainforests are very nice and have lots of plants.
A nd have lots of animals.
I t has lots of trees in it with lots of water,
N ew animals go into the rainforest sometimes.
F lowers growing in some places in the rainforests
O pen space all over the rainforest.
R ainforests all over the world.
E xtraordinary animals dying every day.
S ome trees getting cut down.
T ropical rainforests all over the world.

Dale Richardson (11)
Cochrane Castle Primary School, Johnstone

Rainforest

R ainforests on a rainy day when no one wants to play.
A ll of a sudden the areas are flooding in all of a hurry,
I nsects are fleeing, they might be leaving to find some shelter.
N ow they're back in an awful hurry to get . . .
F lowers to get the pollen before it's fallen.
O pen trees let the sun through so it can shine on you.
R aspberries are sweet, all ready to eat for the animals and insects.
E mergent layer is the sunniest and then the canopy layer.
S tones are sharp, trees are big and animals are scary.
T oads are jumping just like the fire-bellied toad.

Ian Waters (11)
Cochrane Castle Primary School, Johnstone

Rainforest

R ain in the rainforest can measure over 2m.
A ustralian rainforests are the size of 3 football fields.
I n the rainforest trees are getting cut down.
N ature in the rainforest is made for the animals.
F orest frogs hold venom like the fire-bellied frog.
O n the trees live the boa constrictor.
R abbits collect their nuts for their babies.
E lephants are very few in the rainforest.
S nakes are mostly on the forest floor.
T he rainforests can be found all over the world.

Christopher McWilliams (10)
Cochrane Castle Primary School, Johnstone

Rainforest

R ainforests equal an abundance of rain
A lthough they are very warm.
I enjoy studying the rainforests.
N ever anything boring about them.
F lowers to help make medicine.
O xygen to help us breathe.
R egions full of animals in the making.
E xceeds the limit of animals elsewhere.
S lithers, groans all over the rainforests.
T ropical rainforests provide us with food.

Nathan Finlay (10)
Cochrane Castle Primary School, Johnstone

Love

Love is red from every red rose
Love is blue like the sea
Love is yellow like the sun
Love is pink

Love smells of golden bars
Love smells of flowers
Love smells of chocolate

Love sounds like a heart beating that won't ever stop
Love sounds like the day you were together
Love sounds like the last tear

Love tastes like a bag of sugar

Love looks like the time a baby is born
Love looks like the time you propose

Love feels like a warm cuddle
Love feels like you're connected
Love feels like you have a soulmate
Love reminds you of the old times.

Kane Findlay (11)
Commercial Primary School, Dunfermline

38

Sadness

Sadness
Is the colour black
On a cold winter's night
Nipping at your skin.

Sadness
Smells like a rotting lawn
With kids just dropping litter
Wherever they want.

Sadness
Sounds like crying in your ear
Young children screaming and kicking
And children falling over at their school.

Sadness
Tastes like Brussels sprouts
Bitter and horrible making you
Spit them out in the bin.

Sadness
Looks like children
Getting rejected from games
And playing by themselves.

Sadness
Feels like a freezing cold day
And chills moving up
Your spine making
You feel cold all over.

Sadness
Reminds me of getting shouted at
For no reason and people not
Taking interest in me and taking
Interest in other people.

Jack Sutherland (10)
Commercial Primary School, Dunfermline

Pain

The colour of pain is silver,
For the silver knife that damages the skin.
Red is the colour of pain,
When the blood spills over the carpet.

Pain smells like salty tears
As they run down your face.
It smells like blood,
The salty red liquid.

The sound of pain is a clatter
As the bleeding body falls to the ground.
The sound of pain is also a drip
As your blood and tears hit the floor.

Pain's taste is the ground,
The ground you fall in and get hurt.
It also tastes of poison,
As you fall to the ground in pain.

It looks like a screaming man,
Who's just been hurt.
It looks like a sharp knife,
Ready to stab someone.

Pain feels like an axe
Ready to strike something.
Pain feels like acid rain
Burning into your body.

Pain reminds me of people screaming
Wanting the pain to go.
Pain reminds me of a hospital,
People in pain everywhere.

Ryan Neilson (11)
Commercial Primary School, Dunfermline

Love

Love is the colour of red.
Like two hearts as one,
Beating on a beach.

Love smells of strawberries
Freshly picked,
Gushing with taste.

Love sounds like the ocean
Whispering in your ear,
As gently as a butterfly
Flying away softly.

Love tastes like chocolate
Melting in your mouth
On a hot summer's day.

Love looks like smiles
On your face
After having a romantic dinner.

Love feels like cupcakes,
Soft and sweet,
But never horrid.

Love reminds me of true love,
The reason why we don't look
Back at the world
And see how beautiful it is.

Love is powerful
And can never be taken away.

Love.

Ellys Devlin (11)
Commercial Primary School, Dunfermline

Terror

Terror is burgundy
The darkest of all reds,
Trying to splash at you by surprise
And blinding you in the middle.

Terror is the smell of blood,
Blocking your nostrils,
So you can't smell.

Terror is the sound of screams,
Hitting your ears in the dead of night,
Trying to get you out of your bed,
In the middle of a nightmare.

Terror is like tasting fear,
Making your mouth go dry,
You want to get up to get water
But terror stops you.

Terror looks like darkness,
Not being able to see anything,
You think you see something
But it is just your imagination.

Terror feels like being in the shower
Sweat dripping down your face,
Feeling like being cooked up in a cooker.

Terror reminds me of
My worst nightmare
Coming to haunt me again
Like a ghost taking someone to their past.

Michael Maclean (11)
Commercial Primary School, Dunfermline

Love

Love is the colour red,
Like a heart and blood.
Love is also white,
Like a newborn dove.

Love smells like a fresh rose,
Bright red and beautiful.
Love smells like lovely fruits,
Grown by the best fruit farms.

Love sounds like a baby,
Her or his pulse and heart.
Love sounds like a bride and groom
Kissing passionately.

Love tastes like chocolate,
Melted, warm and delicious,
Love tastes like apples,
Sweet, smooth and juicy.

Love looks like your family,
Mum, Dad, grandparents and lovers.
Love looks like your baby,
Smiling up at you.

Love feels like a cushion,
Ever so comfy.
Love feels like blood,
Watery and red.

Love reminds me of my sisters,
The cutest things I'll ever see.

Rebecca Hamilton (11)
Commercial Primary School, Dunfermline

Terror

Terror is yellow
Like big bolts of lightning
But it's also black
Like the night sky

It smells of fear
When people want to cry
It smells of death
And people getting scared.

It sounds like screams
Of people crying for their lives
Terror sounds like cymbals
Getting crashed together.

It tastes bitter
Like too much vinegar
On your fish and chips.

Terror looks like The Scream
Eyes wide and blank
Arid mouth wide ready to scream.

It feels like when you
Get that cold shiver
Trickling down your spine.

Terror reminds me of a
Scared child searching
For its mother.

Ruby Watters (11)
Commercial Primary School, Dunfermline

Pain!

Pain is black like a bat in the night sky
Pain is grey like a storm cloud
Pain is red like running blood
Pain

Pain smells like onions wafting in the breeze
Pain smells of vinegar dripping from a bottle
Pain smells of rotten fish left for months on end
Pain

Pain sounds like a cat scratching a blackboard
Pain sounds like an out of tune guitar
Pain sounds like someone screaming as a dagger goes through their
heart
Pain

Pain tastes like bitter lemons
Pain tastes like pepper
Pain

Pain looks like a river of blood
Pain looks like a knife glinting in the moonlight
Pain

Pain feels like anger building up inside me
Pain feels like a bullet in the chest
Pain

Pain reminds me of blood
Pain reminds me of death
Pain.

Douglas Gourlay (10)
Commercial Primary School, Dunfermline

Love

Love is red
Strong and powerful
Like a ruby red ring
On her finger.

Love smells of roses
Freely sitting in a field
Picked by hand
Smelling ever so sweet.

Love sounds like a heart
Racing so fast
Beyond belief.

Love tastes like chocolate
Sweet and soft
Melts in your mouth.

Love looks like a jungle
Never know which way to go
Look and you may find.

Love feels like a nervous bride
Waiting at home
Husband to be
At the altar.

Love reminds me of
Family together forever
Love!

Lucy Williamson (11)
Commercial Primary School, Dunfermline

Courage

Courage is red like poppies.
For the brave men who fought
In the World War

Courage smells of gunpowder
Like the soldiers
Who are fighting
In Iraq.

Courage sounds like
Planes above you dropping
Bombs on you in
Afghanistan.

Courage tastes like
Blood when you're in
A battle.

Courage looks like,
Tanks, planes and guns
In the wars.

Courage feels like
Doing something great
Like saving a life.

Courage reminds me
Of World Wars 1 and 2
For the people who
Fought in them.

Joshua Mitchell (11)
Commercial Primary School, Dunfermline

Sadness

Sadness is blue
Like the tears I cry.
Sadness is red
Like a heart snapped in half.
Sadness smells of smoke
As I wipe my sore eyes.
Sadness smells of saltwater
That makes me shiver away.
Sadness sounds like shouting,
Children bullying me at school.
Sadness sounds like weeping,
All alone against the crowd.
Sadness tastes like a sour sweet,
Bitter and cruel.
Sadness tastes like mould,
Making me feel sick.
Sadness looks like one tree,
Standing all alone.
Sadness looks like winter,
Cold, bitter, horrid!
Sadness feels like ice
Giving me a burn.
Sadness reminds me of death,
A very upsetting thing.
Sadness is a feeling, there is no doubt,
Sadness is a feeling I could not live without.

Caitlin Sparling (11)
Commercial Primary School, Dunfermline

Happiness

Happiness is
The yellow
Sun beating
Down on the
Children

Happiness smells
Like the nice
Cut grass where
The kids play

Happiness sounds
Like the roar of the
Crowd when you win a race

Happiness tastes of
Your favourite food

Happiness looks
Like your friend's
Smile

Happiness feels
Really nice inside

Happiness reminds
Me of my PS3
When I'm winning
On 'Call of Duty'.

Ross Tyrell (11)
Commercial Primary School, Dunfermline

Happiness

Happiness is the brightest colour in the world
It's so bright it shines like the sun
It never goes dull

Happiness smells like fresh morning air
It fills your lungs with song
It is the freshest air in the world

Happiness sounds like the echo in the shell
It goes on and on and on
It sounds like the moving waves

Happiness tastes like lovely ice cream
Melting in your mouth
The best in the world

Happiness looks like a sunset
Colours all around
Fading slowly

Happiness feels like the beach sand
Soft grass
Glossy silk

Happiness reminds me of smiling faces
All around
That's happiness.

Megan Hill (11)
Commercial Primary School, Dunfermline

Happiness

Happiness is yellow
Like the sun smiling at you
Relieved you're OK.

Happiness smells like grass
Swaying in the wind
Ready for you to lie on it.

Happiness sounds like laughter
From a funny joke
Waiting to be passed on.

Happiness tastes like a lollipop
Sweet and lovely at the same time
Making you want more.

Happiness looks like a kid
On a slide waiting to go on again
Never wanting to stop.

Happiness feels like winning a football match
Knowing you're gonna win
Never gonna lose.

Happiness reminds me of holidays
Relaxing joyfully and just happy
To take your mind off everything.

Ross Hutton (11)
Commercial Primary School, Dunfermline

Love

Love is the colour red
Like when the sun
Is setting.

Love smells like
Roses that are
Blooming.

Love sounds like
Little blue birds
Chirping.

Love tastes like
Breakfast in
Bed in the morning.

Love looks like
The sun in
The sky.

Love feels like
A cuddly toy
Like a bear.

Love reminds me of
Happy children
Playing in the park.

Iona Young (11)
Commercial Primary School, Dunfermline

Happiness

Happiness is orange,
Like the middle of a daffodil
Blowing in the breeze.

Happiness sounds like
Children laughing and having fun
On a lovely day.

Happiness feels like
Nothing in the world can stop you
Having fun.

Happiness looks like
Smiles on everyone's face
And never a frown.

Happiness tastes like
Sweet summer,
Everyone's favourite season.

Happiness smells like
Freshly picked flowers
From the garden patch.

Happiness reminds me of
Making the most of life
And trying to make people happy.

Emma Hill (11)
Commercial Primary School, Dunfermline

Joy

Joy is orange like the Eglin Star strip.
Joy is multicoloured like the rainbow I see.
Joy is yellow like the midday sun.

Joy smells of a fresh drink of water.
Joy smells of a new car.
Joy smells of a brand new football trick.

Joy sounds like a crowd cheering.
Joy sounds like a speeding racing car.
Joy sounds like a gun firing.

Joy tastes like an Italian pizza.
Joy tastes like fresh carrot.
Joy tastes like rhubarb fool.

Joy looks like a happy face.
Joy looks like a ball in a goal.
Joy looks like a million pounds.

Joy feels like winning a match.
Joy feels like having my heart's desire.
Joy feels like a laser gun game.

Joy reminds me of the goals I score.
Joy reminds me of when I won a race.
Joy reminds me of a football game.

Robert MacPhee (11)
Commercial Primary School, Dunfermline

Terror

Terror is red for blood.

Terror smells like the breath
Of a vicious animal
Or it smells like
Fear.

It sounds like people
Screaming when
They're getting attacked
By something.

You can taste the
Fear of terror.

It looks like someone
Getting attacked right in front
Of you and you think
You're next.

It feels like someone
Grabbing your arm
And dragging you somewhere.

It reminds me of losing
My gran at a fair.

Thomas MacKenzie (10)
Commercial Primary School, Dunfermline

Love

Love is the colour of you
And you look so blue

But you smell like shampoo
And you're the same as love

Love sounds like you
With your voice so new
And you're the best thing I've heard

Love tastes so new
Just like that cherry on you
With cream on it too
It would be like you

Love looks like you
With that lovely smile
And those green eyes

It feels like you
When I am holding your hands
So warm like you're me
That's why you're with me.

Love always reminds me of you
Love, love oh it is you.

Callum McKinnon (10)
Commercial Primary School, Dunfermline

Happiness

Happiness is yellow like the sun.
Happiness is the colour blue like the sky.
Happiness is the colour green like the grass.

Happiness smells like fizzy juice and sweets.
Happiness smells like flowers.
Happiness smells like friendship.

Happiness sounds like laughter and joy.
Happiness sounds wonderful and happy.
Happiness sounds exciting and surprising.

Happiness tastes like chocolate.
Happiness tastes like friendship.
Happiness tastes like children playing.

Happiness looks like fun and playfulness.
Happiness looks like friendship.
Happiness looks like children playing.

Happiness feels like a kid catching you in a game.
Happiness feels like a friend shaking your hand.
Happiness feels like your mum patting your back.

Happiness reminds me of when I went up to Shetland.
Happiness reminds me of my friends.

Nathan Grogan (11)
Commercial Primary School, Dunfermline

Terror

Terror is black as coal
Terror is the red of someone's blood
Terror is navy blue, the colour of the night.

Terror is the smell of rotting meat
Terror is the smell of death
Terror is the smell of decomposing food.

Terror is a piercing scream
Terror is the screech of a bat
Terror is a shattering yell.

Terror's taste is ice cold
Terror's taste is horrible
Terror's taste is nasty and mean.

Terror looks like the darkest cave
Terror looks like the sharpest fang on a Bengal tiger.

Terror feels like a needle through your heart
Terror feels like a splitting headache.

Terror will remind you of pain and misery
Terror will bring back horror.

Terror is the darkest moment.

Rebecca Emslie (11)
Commercial Primary School, Dunfermline

Love

Love is pink
Like every petal
On a beautiful rose
Love smells of perfume
On a sunny day
At the seaside
Love sounds like
A heart beating
When someone is about to kiss you
Love tastes like
Rich Belgium chocolate
Melting in your mouth
Love looks like
Two happy birds
Singing merrily in a tree
Love feels like
A silk top on the washing line
Ready to be worn
Love reminds me of
Two happy teenagers
Having fun!

Tempany Grace (11)
Commercial Primary School, Dunfermline

Silence

The colour of silence is very light blue
Every one is frozen
There's not an echo in the air.

Silence smells like a silent church's candles
The wax burning away.

It sounds like a dark empty room
With not a soul in sight.

Tasting silence is a cold bitter taste.
Someone is angry and not going to talk.

Silence looks like a dark empty cave.
Black in the night
Not a bat in sight.

It feels like someone has betrayed you
There's no happiness left in the world.

Silence reminds me of icicles in a cave
The only noise is the water dripping from the ice.

Sam Morman (11)
Commercial Primary School, Dunfermline

Terror

Terror is black
It smells like fear
And it sounds like death.
Terror tastes like cold meat
It looks like death
And feels like bones.
It reminds me of horror movies.

Cameron Mitchell (11)
Commercial Primary School, Dunfermline

Courage

Courage is a stately silver like a knight in shining armour.
Courage is also a bold blue like the deep blue ocean.

Courage feels like you're on top of the world
And that no one can beat you.

Courage smells of fresh air and adventure.
It also smells of bravery and power.

Courage sounds like the wind rustling in the trees
Or a wolf's deep howl.

Courage tastes like a juicy steak loin, so soft and tender.

Courage looks like a still wood, silent lush and calm
Or a tiger so big and powerful.

Courage reminds me of a knight in shining armour
Or maybe a large spacious field
Oh so free.

Lauren Russell (10)
Commercial Primary School, Dunfermline

Happiness

Happiness is golden like a child's thoughts on their birthday.

Happiness smells like wrapping paper after it has been torn apart
To reveal the present within.

Happiness sounds like a child's squeal of delight
When they realise they have got the present they wanted.

Happiness tastes like a chocolate sponge cake cut into little slices.

Happiness looks like the smile on a child's face when they have had
a good time.

Happiness feels like a teddy you hug at night.

Happiness reminds me of a birthday party I had a long time ago.

Malcolm Ross (11)
Commercial Primary School, Dunfermline

Love

Love is like a rainbow shining in the sky
So pretty and beautiful and bright.

Love smells of roses and violets and daisies too
And it smells of chocolate for you.

Love sounds like little bells jingling all night
And love sounds like birds twittering,
Flittering all over the morning light.

Love tastes of chocolates, all sorts of types and also tastes of love
made just for you.

Love looks like laughter from a child in the park
Playing with her family until it is dark.

Love feels like you can't hold in your heart because it belongs to
another or like a dad holding his first child.

Love reminds me of my childhood and when I first saw you.

Eve Paterson (10)
Commercial Primary School, Dunfermline

Love!

Love is bright red like a heart of chocolate.
Love is yellow like the shimmering sun.

Love sounds like two love birds in the tree.
Love sounds like kissing in the winter.
Love sounds like laughter all around.

Love feels like someone about to kiss you.
Love feels like a mother holding their first child's hand.

Love tastes like chocolate melting in your mouth.
Love tastes like joy all around.

Love smells like roses all around.
Love smells like violets in your vases.

Love reminds me of me and Ryan kissing for the first time.

Angela Miller (10)
Commercial Primary School, Dunfermline

The Wild Dog

He seemed to know the savannah.
He was the leader of the pack.
His teeth chopping through the prey's skin.

His stamina helps him run for hours after his prey,
His eyes glare like burning fireballs
As he waves goodbye to his pups,
They go and find their own pack.
He is part-dog and part-hare,
Part neither . . . for his wildness.

Aidan Stephenson (10)
Dalton Listerdale J&I School, Rotherham

The Panda Bear

He seemed to know the forest
So strong he strode,
His fur
Like a soft pillow
It ran so heavily through the Amazon.

His eyes were colourful
And tampered
And light black,
And as he passed through the lake
He swam in the lake so blue
And I saw his wet smooth fur slowly
Coming out the lake,
With his food from the bottom.

Then out in the Amazon
With the round fur,
Smoothly striding
Lithely,
Strongly,
He walked . . .
That brave bear,
Softly, tampered, white and black,
Part-bear, part-tiger,
Part neither . . . for his blood was brave.

Matthew Hill (11) & Bradley
Dalton Listerdale J&I School, Rotherham

The Dolphin

She seems to know the sea,
Like her own kingdom.
Her skin is
As soft as a feather,
She is sweeter than
Candyfloss.

Her fins are as soft
And tapered
And aqua blue
Her teeth are as white as
Paper
Her eyes are dark blue.

Then out in his kingdom
With that 3 cornered fin
So bravely
So sweet that blue soft loving aqua
Fish swam deep into her kingdom.

Zaynah Choudry
Dalton Listerdale J&I School, Rotherham

The Wolf

He seems to know the forest
So stealthily he runs;
His teeth
Like daggers piercing your skin,
His eyes glare right at you like burning fireballs
His ears can hear you whisper from miles away
He sits all alone under the moon howling all night
This man-eating beast is ready to hunt for its bloody meal
Its blanket of fur is as soft as a pillow, it has a damp nose
Which can help sniff out blood
That's how it catches its prey
Quite violently with blood surrounding the wolf
It only hunts at night, that's why it is hardly heard or seen
Darkness breaks, moon awakes
Brown deer very near, it is brought down full of fear
Deadly bite, very tight
Every wolf will feast tonight.

Tom Parkin (10) & Reece
Dalton Listerdale J&I School, Rotherham

The Meerkats

They seemed to know the enclosure
So leisurely they ran.
Their legs
Were like pieces of twig.
They were thin and strong
With cute eyes.

Pranced,
Skipped,
Danced,
They could dig with a blindfold over the eyes,
They sucked up a juicy worm,
As they were in the enclosure,
They looked up on the lights in the
Enclosure and thought they could escape
To a hot country,
So they did.

Hannah Roberts (10) & Niamh (10)
Dalton Listerdale J&I School, Rotherham

Pocket Money

As fast as a cheetah
I do all my chores
For a shiny pound for my money box.

I love bright shiny pounds
Which I can get
For my collection.

My mom gives me the pound
I save the pound to get
Some of my favourite things.

I want all the pounds
Which I can get
For all kinds of things.

Rhys Glazzard (10)
Ham Dingle Primary School, Stourbridge

Money, Money

Money, money how do you spend me?
Do you save me or do you spend me?
Fresh, crisp and from the bank,
Straight from the cashpoint tank.

Glinting and glistening like the sun,
Letting someone spend me with fantastic fun,
There are no smudges, tatters or tears,
So try to give me to someone that cares.

Tumbling into a heap of cash,
Like a king's secret treasure stash,
In the dark, spooky purse I stay,
There I wait till the special day,
A fumbling hand picks me up,
And places me on the counter for all to see.
It buys a hot cup of tea,
And in its place, exchanges me!

Emily Reeve (10)
Ham Dingle Primary School, Stourbridge

Money Can't Buy

Money can't buy you love when your precious tiny heart is broken.
Money can't buy you friendship when you've had a serious war with
your friend.
Money can't buy you happiness when the whole human race has
turned against you.
Money can't buy you health when your body is about to die a deathly
death.
Money can't buy you peace when you are being attacked.
Money can't buy brainpower when you feel broken down and have
run out of fuel.
Money can't buy you good luck when your life is closing down and
wearing way.
Money can't always buy you what you want.

Jessica Wildsmith (10)
Ham Dingle Primary School, Stourbridge

Money, Money, Money!

Glittering, glistening, glinting,
I sit there on the table like a golden and glowing hot sun,
I am a new coin of course, being spent is so much fun!

Smooth, sharp and silky that is me,
I dance around the pink wallet singing with glee,
I feel so divine here
I don't want to be spent in a million years.

But soon we both get passed around, fiver, tenner and a pound!

Grotty, grimy, grubby I am
It's so unfair, I'm only 1 pound!
I get passed around every day, my feelings still full of dismay!

Scrunched, sweaty and smudged now that is me,
I'm such a lonely child.

No one wants me!

Isaac Milne (10)
Ham Dingle Primary School, Stourbridge

Keep Your Money Safe

Keep your money tight
In your pocket,
And put it in the bank!
Or in the safe,
Put your card in the wall,
And you have some money,
It is so, so brilliant.
When you don't get money out,
Or if you do, put it in the safe,
Or the bank, keep it safe in your
Pocket and take it to the bank to be safe!

Jamie Johnson (10)
Ham Dingle Primary School, Stourbridge

If I Was A Millionaire

If I was a millionaire
I would buy a fast, cool car,
Which would be a shiny red Ferrari.

If I was a millionaire,
I would buy as many diamonds as possible,
I would be showered in them.

If I was a millionaire,
I would buy a massive, fun garden.
Which would be as big as a football pitch.

If I was a millionaire,
It wouldn't be fair,
Because everyone else wouldn't be a millionaire,
So I would have to share.

Jordan Uppal (10)
Ham Dingle Primary School, Stourbridge

What Money Can't Buy You . . .

Money can't buy you smiles, when you are alone, melancholy and
neglected.
Money can't buy you love, when you're distressed and sorrowful.
Money can't buy you strength, while you are meek and feeble.
Money can't buy you peace, when there is an invasion between
others.
Money can't buy you sunshine, on a starless and shadowy night.
Money can't buy you health, when you are frail and tender.
Money can't buy you happiness, when you are mournful and
heartbroken.
That is what money cannot buy.

Lucy Brammer (10)
Ham Dingle Primary School, Stourbridge

The Pound Coin Goes Everywhere

The pound coin goes everywhere,
It goes out of Mum's purse to me,
Then I give it to the shopkeeper,
I swap it for chocolate with glee.

Like a car my pound goes everywhere,
Now it is in the till,
When I go outside, it is raining, I run,
Then stop, there's a shiny pound, I pick it up,
Now all day I should get good luck!
As quick as a racing car I run.

Ella Lucy Jones (10)
Ham Dingle Primary School, Stourbridge

If I Was A Millionaire!

If I was a millionaire,
I would spend my money wisely,
I know I can't spend it on everything,
But I can lend and get back,
So don't be a fool, be careful,
What you spend your money on.
I know I really like shiny, sparkly,
Clean and bright money,
But if I really was a millionaire,
I would share and be fair.

Megan Giles (10)
Ham Dingle Primary School, Stourbridge

My Best Friend's Life

Mum gives a textured pound to Dan who rides the bus,
My pound, like a bird goes everywhere,
The bus driver puts my pound in his cash register,
My pound is my best friend who stays by my side,
My grandma asks for two, one pound coins.
For a two pound coin,
And then gives it to me for my birthday,
My pound coin goes everywhere like an aeroplane in the swirly,
                                                    sparkly sky.

Amanda Bryce (11)
Ham Dingle Primary School, Stourbridge

Money Can Be . . .

Money can be as fresh as the frosty air on my face.
Money can be as crisp as scarlet falling leaves in autumn.
Money can be as smooth as a velvety wedding dress.
Money can be as torn as an old top being ripped to pieces.
Money can be as crinkled as a piece of paper that's been
                                    folded and folded.
Money can be as damaged as a shattered vase in pieces
                                        on the floor.
Money can be as golden as the rising summer sun.

Aimee Price (11)
Ham Dingle Primary School, Stourbridge

Money Is

Money can be as fresh as frosty air hitting my face.
Money can be as crisp as autumn leaves falling in autumn.
Money can be as smooth as a velvety wedding dress.
Money can be as sharp as a sword being wielded.
Money can be pristine and precious like a newborn baby.
But money can also be tattered like a pair of old shoes.

Ben Smith (10)
Ham Dingle Primary School, Stourbridge

What Money Can't Buy

Money can't buy you happiness when the human race is against you.
Money can't buy the world peace when there's a dangerous,
                                    vile war.
Money can't buy you sunshine on a gloomy, depressing morning.
Money can't buy you friendship when you're alone in the
                                    gargantuan world.
Money can't buy you smiles when you're down in the dumps.
Money can't buy you health when you're shivery and diseased.
That's what money can't buy.

Jack Wootton (10)
Ham Dingle Primary School, Stourbridge

At The Bank

At the bank I put money away for a rainy day.
At the bank I take some out and put more in
With the glimmer of silver, shimmer of gold.

At the bank there's money everywhere.
I would have some more but I wouldn't dare take what's not mine.

At the bank I give them money to pay the tax
Then pounds and pennies paying for important things
So if I had more money I would be rich.

Connor Smith (10)
Ham Dingle Primary School, Stourbridge

Money Can Be . . .

Money can be as fresh as air on my face.
Money can be as crisp as golden, falling leaves in the autumn.
Money can be as smooth as a silky wedding dress.
Money can be as silky as a king's velvet cape.
Money can be as sharp as a huge butcher's knife.
But money can be torn as easily as a delicate spring-green leaf.

Laura Dimmock (10)
Ham Dingle Primary School, Stourbridge

Money In My Pocket

Money in my pocket,
Money in my mom's,
Money in my uncle's
Money is so sparkly!

Everyone knows it,
Not many people show it,
Spend it wisely or,
Keep it very tightly!

Callum Bodycote (10)
Ham Dingle Primary School, Stourbridge

Finding Money

Pennies here
Coins over there
Pounds on the floor
Money everywhere
I touch it, I feel like a millionaire
Should I keep it?
Should I not?
Should I go to the candy shop?

Callum Hall (10)
Ham Dingle Primary School, Stourbridge

The Pound That Goes Everywhere

Like a roller coaster my pound goes everywhere
My pound spends like I'm a millionaire
It never ends, it never ends
My pound goes all around town
Like a train goes round a circle track
My pound turns into sweets
My pound is spent.

Casey Dawes (10)
Ham Dingle Primary School, Stourbridge

What Is Money?

Money is the fresh, golden pound like the bright yellow sun glistening
in the sky.
Money is a crisp, smooth note that sits in my wallet like a precious,
pearl shut tight within an ocean clam.
Money is pristine and shiny sleeping in a till waiting to be swapped
and spent.
Money is soon tattered and torn, by being passed around and
around, until it's lost in a pocket.

Georgia Cox (11)
Ham Dingle Primary School, Stourbridge

What Money Can't Buy

Money can't buy you sunshine
When you are in the middle of a cheerless, unhappy day.
Money can't buy you peace
When you are in the middle of a frightening, dreaded war.
Money can't buy you happiness
When you are gloomy and heartbroken.
Money can't buy you friendship
When you are neglected and lonely.

Jessica Scott (10)
Ham Dingle Primary School, Stourbridge

Money Can Be . . .

Money can be as fresh as the cold frosty air on my face.
Money can be as crisp as scarlet and golden leaves
falling in autumn.
Money can be as smooth as a white velvety wedding dress.
Money can be as golden as the warm bright sun.
Money can be as glistening as a pearl necklace.
Money can be as glittering as the moonlight in an inky black sky.

Ellie Green (10)
Ham Dingle Primary School, Stourbridge

Money Can't Buy You . . .

Money can't buy you sunshine on a damp and drizzly day.
Money can't buy you smiles when you feel melancholy
and distressed.
Money can't buy you a family when you are alone.
Money can't buy you friendship when you are neglected and lonely.
Money can't buy you peace when you are at war with others.
That is what money can't buy.

Estelle Jones (10)
Ham Dingle Primary School, Stourbridge

Money Can't Buy . . .

Money can't buy you friendship when it feels like the world is lonely
and against you.
Money can't buy you sunshine on a wet, cold and misty night.
Money can't buy you love when you're on your own, sorrowful in
the darkness.
Money can't buy you smiles when you're alone, ashamed and guilty.

Ella-Jay Hingley (11)
Ham Dingle Primary School, Stourbridge

Money Is . . .

Money can be as fresh as the frosty air in my face.
Money can be as crisp as autumn falling leaves.
Money can be as smooth as a velvety wedding dress.
Money can be as golden as the hot sand on the beach.
But money can also be as torn as ripped and battered clothes.

Charlotte Kings (10)
Ham Dingle Primary School, Stourbridge

If I Was A Millionaire

If I was a millionaire I would buy a flat screen TV.
If I was a millionaire I would buy every game console.
If I was a millionaire I would buy a mansion as hard as gold.
If I was a millionaire I would buy a golden bathtub.
If I was a millionaire I would buy a golden stretch limo.

Ethan James (10)
Ham Dingle Primary School, Stourbridge

If I Could

If I could buy happiness I would.
If I could buy rain for Africa I would.
If I could buy a house for homeless people I would.
If I could buy kindness I really would.
If I could buy love I wish I could.

Aaron Aseltine (11)
Ham Dingle Primary School, Stourbridge

Money Can Be

Money can be as fresh as a daisy,
Money can be as crisp as auburn falling leaves in autumn,
Money can be as smooth as silky shark skin.
Money can be as sharp as a fox's tooth.
Money can be as pristine as a new car.

William Smith (10)
Ham Dingle Primary School, Stourbridge

If I Had Wings

(Based on 'If I had wings' by Pie Corbett)

If I had wings
I would listen
to the miaowing of
the cute cat.

If I had wings
I would touch
the angels which are
as beautiful as golden diamonds.

If I had wings
I would breathe
in the lovely cold air
that is as delicious as sweet roses.

If I had wings
I would gaze
at the thunder and lightning
booming in the stormy sky.

If I had wings
I would taste
a slice of summer
that is as hot as pepperoni.

If I had wings
I would dream
of skiing the seas
and walking the ocean.

Lauren Wood (8)
Holy Family RC Primary School, Preston

If I Had Wings

(Based on 'If I had wings' by Pie Corbett)

If I had wings
I would listen to the
Fireworks whizzing
And whirling in the air.

If I had wings
I would touch
The blazing hot sun which is
As hot as the heat of a typhoon.

If I had wings
I would breathe in the scent of chicken
Curry oozing in my dreams.

If I had wings
I would gaze
At warbling waves pounding on the rocks.

If I had wings
I would taste
A lump of lavender as lovely as lightning liquorice.

If I had wings
I would dream of
Kayaking the hills
And hiking the Pacific Ocean.

William Dixon (8)
Holy Family RC Primary School, Preston

If I Had Wings

(Based on 'If I had wings' by Pie Corbett)

If I had wings
I would listen to the horse
Squealing in the forest.

If I had wings
I would touch
The sand as hot as the sun in Egypt.

If I had wings
I would breathe
In melting ice cream as it floats.

If I had wings
I would gaze
At the barking puppy playing with a bone.

If I had wings
I would taste
A slab of scuba diving
Moist as a strawberry.

If I had wings
I would dream
Of swimming the forest
And hiking the oceans.

Harry Dunsmuir (7)
Holy Family RC Primary School, Preston

If I Had Wings

(Based on 'If I had wings' by Pie Corbett)

If I had wings
I would touch
The fluffy clouds
Which are as soft as snow.

If I had wings
I would breathe in
The first rose petal
Growing on a thorn bush.

If I had wings
I would gaze
At the playful puppy
As it plays with its ball.

If I had wings
I would taste
An orange peach
As juicy as a jelly.

If I had wings
I would dream
Of swimming the deserts
And walking the seas.

Nicole Bamber (7)
Holy Family RC Primary School, Preston

My Magic Roman Box

(Based on 'Magic Box' by Kit Wright)

I will put in my box . . .
A sharp, silver dagger
The scraping of the strigil

I will put in my box . . .
A lion who is
As strong as a Roman
A Roman who is
As strong as Zeus

I will put in my box . . .
The shouting of strong Boudicca
The cracking of the stone statue
A white scaly fish
A slimy, slippery mouse brain

My box is made from mice and metal
With stones on the lid
And catapults in the corners
Its hinges are made from catapult stones

I shall jump in my box
On the big bouncy trampoline
Then I will daydream about the Romans.

Rylan Thompson (8)
Holy Family RC Primary School, Preston

If I Had Wings

(Based on 'If I had wings' by Pie Corbett)

If I had wings
I would listen
To the crocodile going *snap* in the jungle.

If I had wings
I would touch
The moon which is as shiny as a diamond.

If I had wings
I would breathe
Crispy bacon as it sizzles through my head.

If I had wings
I would gaze
At the slithering snake in the forest.

If I had wings
I would taste
A map of the moon
Which is as yummy as cheese.

If I had wings
I would dream of
Surfing the mountains and hiking the coral.

Matthew Greenidge (7)
Holy Family RC Primary School, Preston

If I Had Wings

(Based on 'If I had wings' by Pie Corbett)

If I had wings
I would listen
To the bells dinging and donging.

If I had wings
I would touch
The blazing hot sun which is as round as a beach ball.

If I had wings
I would breathe
The scent of chicken Kiev as it gets stuck to the pan.

If I had wings
I would taste
A chunk of China which is as hot as chicken curry.

If I had wings
I would gaze
At the crashing waves at the seaside.

If I had wings
I would dream of swimming the mountains
And skiing the swimming pool.

Chloe Lyon (7)
Holy Family RC Primary School, Preston

If I Had Wings

(Based on 'If I had wings' by Pie Corbett)

If I had wings
I would listen
To my rubber ball
Sizzling in the sun.

If I had wings
I would touch
The universe that is as big
As all of the planets put together.

If I had wings
I would breathe
In my seeds falling down from the
Biggest flower in the world.

If I had wings
I would gaze
At the snowflakes swirling
Down from the white sky.

Bradley Neild (7)
Holy Family RC Primary School, Preston

A Clown Collector

(Based on 'The Sound Collector' by Roger McGough)

A clown came this evening
Dressed all in yellow and blue
Put all the senses in a ball
And bounced them to the zoo.

The kicking of the kangaroo
The swinging of the tail
The roaring of the tiger
The slithering of the snail.

The plopping of the rain
The miaowing of the cat
The clattering of the horses
The squeaking of the rat.

A clown came this evening
He didn't leave his name
Left us only silence
Life will never be the same.

Amy Jo Newman (8)
Holy Family RC Primary School, Preston

If I Had Wings

(Based on 'If I had wings' by Pie Corbett)

If I had wings
I would look at the growling bull chasing after the man.

If I had wings
I would listen to the tiger roaring in the zoo.

If I had wings
I would touch the white soft clouds as comfy as a pillow.

If I had wings
I would taste a slice of snake as delicious as swirling spaghetti.

If I had wings
I would dream of scuba diving the mountains and hiking the lakes.

Caitlin Baldwin (7)
Holy Family RC Primary School, Preston

Guess What I Saw!

A snake in a lake,
A seal having a meal,
A cow doing a bow,
A fox in a box,
A snail in jail,
A goat with a coat,
A sheep having a sleep,
A shark in a park,
A dog in a fog,
A fly eating pie,
A bee in the sea,
A mouse in a house,
A fish in a dish,
A parrot eating a carrot,
An owl with a towel,
A deer is here.

Maria Nicol (7)
Kirkhill Primary School, Aberdeen

Seasons

Spring is green:
Like the incredible Hulk from Spider-Man,
Like a slimy frog jumping in and out of a pond,
Like a juicy grape,
Like a hard, tough crocodile.

Summer is red:
Like a noisy fire engine,
Like a wooden pencil,
Like a small robin red breast on Christmas morning,
Like a traffic light above amber and green.

Autumn is brown:
Like yummy sweet chocolate,
Like spray-on fake tan,
Like a brown, crunchy leaf,
Like my mum's long hair.

Winter is white:
Like a fluffy cloud,
Like a rubber on the end of a pencil,
Like a furry polar bear,
Like a woolly sheep.

Zak Cartney (8)
Kirkhill Primary School, Aberdeen

Colours Of The Rainbow

Blue like the cool water,
Pink like a nice jellyfish,
Red like a red rose that's beautiful,
Green like sweet green grass,
Yellow like the sun that's bright,
Purple like the sweet plums,
Orange like a pumpkin at Hallowe'en.

Josh Corbett (7)
Kirkhill Primary School, Aberdeen

The Rhyme Shop

In our shop we sell anything:
Blue shoes,
Bright lights,
Big pigs,
Shrinking drinks,
Metal petals,
Cat mats,
Cute suits,
Great skates,
Nice mice,
Red beds,
Good food,
Mean beans,
Boys' toys,
Cook books,
Sorry we don't sell milk.

Shelley Milne (8)
Kirkhill Primary School, Aberdeen

Relatives I Have Known

Of all the relatives I have met,
Here are a few I can't forget,
Uncle Paul is very tall,
Grandpa Jo is very slow,
Uncle Kevin is only seven,
Uncle Roy is filled with joy,
Grandma Praty eats chicken satay,
Aunt Kelly is so smelly,
Uncle Roland went to Poland,
Aunt Morane went to Spain,
But the strangest relative I've ever seen,
Is Uncle Joe who looks like Mr Bean.

Connor Forbes (8)
Kirkhill Primary School, Aberdeen

10 Things Your Parents Would Never Say

Put on make-up
Stay up late
Please yourself
Take the day off
Wear what you want
Trash your room
Buy what you please
Paint your room
Have a party
Take my DS.

Lauren Riddell (8)
Kirkhill Primary School, Aberdeen

Monster Croc

M y monster croc is a baby croc,
O n Monday it was so hot so I took him swimming,
N o one was scared of him because the croc was very nice,
S ocs is his name, he never runs away,
T anks of water he drinks every day,
E very day he goes out to play in the garden,
R oxy is my neighbour's dog, he is very good to play with.

C lear smell to sense danger,
R ough feeling to touch,
O ily water he feels like,
C old water he lives in.

Ellys Clark (8)
Kirkhill Primary School, Aberdeen

Move It

Fingers wiggle,
Feet stomp,
Elbows bend,
Eyes blink,
Teeth bite,
Hands clap,
Arms wave,
Noses smell,
Hearts beat,
Legs walk,
I need to get moving.

Shannon Shearer (7)
Kirkhill Primary School, Aberdeen

My Dog

Fast-runner
Heavy-sleeper
Dog-lover
Slow-walker
Toy-chewer
People-watcher
Mud-roller
Rain-hater
Sun-lover.

Declan Small (10)
Kirkhill Primary School, Aberdeen

Mary Had Some Bubblegum

Mary had some bubblegum,
It was big and sky-blue.
Then she went to Asda Price and
Lost it in the queue.

Dillon King (9)
Kirkhill Primary School, Aberdeen

Fear! · Cinquain

Sleeping.
I hear the door.
Now I open the door.
Nothing except a little note . . .
Just blank.

Ellie Wallace (10)
Kirkhill Primary School, Aberdeen

Pirates

Pirates, pirates, pirates,
Naked, negative, nasty pirates,
Busy, brilliant, blue pirates,
Skinny, scary, stinky pirates,
Pirates, pirates, pirates.

Yasmin Le Tissier (8)
Kirkhill Primary School, Aberdeen

Hunter · Cinquain

Slither,
Through the dead leaves,
Hunter hunting for food,
Very quiet, approach the prey,
Then strike!

Grant Laird (10)
Kirkhill Primary School, Aberdeen

Night · Haiku

Sweet dreams in my head.
Snuggled up in my warm bed.
Dark as the night falls.

Ailsa Dickson (10)
Kirkhill Primary School, Aberdeen

Courage

Courage tastes like cake when you are about to
Take over your fears and do what you have always feared doing.
Courage looks like you are the bravest person on Earth,
About to do all you can to take over your fears.
Courage reminds me of my mum being stung
By more than one thousand wasps.
When she came home, she'd overcome her fear of wasps.
Courage feels like you could do anything
After you have taken over your fears.
Courage smells like you could just breathe in
And you could do anything.
Courage sounds like silence,
Like you don't hear anything when you are facing your fear.

Rhianna Ball (8)
Langford Lower School, Langford

Courage

Courage sounds like Indiana Jones
Shouting, 'I'm going in!'
Courage smells of fierce burning fire
With firemen trying to extinguish it.
Courage looks like a man fighting a lion.
Courage reminds me of when
My dad picked up a grass snake.
Courage tastes like marshmallows
In a haunted forest.
Courage feels like a man going into
A bug-infested cave to save a woman.

Ben Tarttelin (8)
Langford Lower School, Langford

Courage

Courage smells like my skin,
Because you can't smell it.
Courage looks like Superman
Dodging a million bullets.
Courage feels like being brave
When I defeat an army.
Courage sounds like my heart
Beating as fast as an ant.
Courage tastes like sleeping
In a haunted bed and a haunted house.

Hobie Ip (8)
Langford Lower School, Langford

Courage

Courage feels like being
Excited before a performance.
Courage reminds me of when
I performed my gymnastics
In front of my parents.
Courage smells of
Roasted marshmallows
Over a campfire.
Courage tastes like sweet
Cotton candy melting in my mouth.

Lauren Hilleard (9)
Langford Lower School, Langford

Anger

Anger tastes like smoke and dirty danger.
Anger looks like perfect people are all stressed as they fight.
Anger smells of frightening fire burning
And going everywhere, and people screaming.
Anger reminds me of people fighting
And people frowning and hurting each other.
Anger feels like blood going everywhere
And people getting stressed.
Anger sounds like people shouting,
Screaming and nobody having fun.

Natasha Beaton (8)
Langford Lower School, Langford

Happiness

Happiness looks like children are having fun.
Happiness feels like playing football on a Sunday morning.
Happiness smells like pancakes on a Saturday morning.
Happiness sounds like children shouting across the park.

Joshua Kell (8)
Langford Lower School, Langford

Anger

Anger tastes like smoke drifting from the fiery sky.
Anger reminds me of getting upset and bombs coming down.
Anger feels all dirty and horrible, like
Everything inside you is burning up.
Anger sounds like danger is coming,
It feels like getting upset.
Anger looks like smoke going through the clouds
Away from the air.
Anger smells like fire burning badly in the backyard.

Eleanor Manning (8)
Langford Lower School, Langford

Fun

Fun tastes like air after school at the park.
Fun looks like people crayfishing at the lake at 5pm.
Fun feels like an adrenalin rush
On a motorbike on a Sunday.
Fun reminds me of Alton Towers -
The Spinball Whizzer when it first opens.
Fun smells like sweat on a vest,
Running around playing football at Wembley.

Gino Menga (8)
Langford Lower School, Langford

Silence

Silence smells of melted chocolate drifting me to sleep.
Silence tastes like a box of honey nut cornflakes
Getting me up for breakfast.
Silence sounds like air brushing through my head.
Silence reminds me of both my rabbits in their graves.
Silence looks like darkness at midnight.
Silence feels like flies flying at me with fear.

Cole Martin (8)
Langford Lower School, Langford

Surprise

Surprise feels like ants crawling in my tiny little tummy.
Surprise looks like the present you have been wanting for years.
Surprise smells of chocolate, wrapping paper and sweets.
Surprise tastes like toffee shocks with honey inside,
Sucking and then suddenly it pops!
Surprise reminds me of all the fun I've had over the days.
Surprise feels like playing on the drop tower,
Then suddenly going down.

Katie Hunter Shaw (8)
Langford Lower School, Langford

Surprise

Surprise sounds like the sun fizzing in the sky.
Surprise reminds me of Christmas when
Reindeer come past the rainbow and deliver presents.
Surprise tastes of chunky chocolate melting in your mouth.
Surprise looks like going to watch an exciting football match.
Surprise smells like Coke fizzing up and bubbling.
Surprise feels like sweating hands slithering down a hill.

Nathan Hodge (9)
Langford Lower School, Langford

Happiness

Happiness feels like a soft, cuddly teddy.
Happiness sounds like people rushing through a river.
Happiness tastes like a chocolate cake on a birthday.
Happiness looks like children playing at the funfair.
Happiness reminds me of Christmas presents.
Happiness smells like Easter eggs, chocolatey and creamy.
Happiness looks like a hot Hawaiian holiday hut on a humid day.

Summer Wilson (8)
Langford Lower School, Langford

Fun

Fun feels like opening presents on my birthday.
Fun tastes like popcorn in the microwave.
Fun smells like my times tables best.
Fun looks like a swimming pool in my house.
Fun reminds me of my mum and dad.
Fun sound like the sound of the telly.

Caitlin Albert (9)
Langford Lower School, Langford

Sadness

Sadness looks like a lot of dull colours bursting out.
Sadness feels like I have lost all my friends
And that I have nobody to play with.
Sadness smells of horrible, manky food.
Sadness sounds like people dying in the war.
Sadness reminds me of my cat dying.

Katie White (9)
Langford Lower School, Langford

Silence

Silence sounds like watching a waterfall
From a long distance.
Silence feels like not talking.
Silence smells of cold air.
Silence tastes like warm water.
Silence reminds me of floating flowers.

Anna McKinlay (8)
Langford Lower School, Langford

Happiness

Happiness tastes like chocolate log on a Christmas Day.
Happiness smells like pizza on a plate in front of you.
Happiness sounds like children giggling in the park.
Happiness feels like my dog snuggling up to me.
Happiness reminds me of when I picked my dog up
On the way home from my holiday.

Bailey Cheek (8)
Langford Lower School, Langford

Silence

Silence feels like a flapping, flying, fat bird falling from a tree.
Silence sounds like a safari park swimming to sea.
Silence reminds you of rabbits running around.
Silence looks like love, lightning and light.
Silence tastes like tummies trying to eat.
Silence smells like swaying slowly in the street.

Mya Huntley (8)
Langford Lower School, Langford

Silence

Silence reminds me of a dead person
Floating up to Heaven.
Silence sounds like someone falling to
The ground in slow motion.
Silence makes me feel like I am sleeping.

Daniel Gibbens (9)
Langford Lower School, Langford

Fun

Fun looks like a big ceremony about to happen.
Fun sounds like a big bang.
Fun reminds me of me and my dad going fishing.
Fun feels like flopping up and down.
Fun tastes like a tin of tomatoes splattering through the lid.

Ben Gibbs (8)
Langford Lower School, Langford

Sadness

Sadness tastes like burning hot fire
Blazing ginormous cities and forests.
Sadness smells like smoke.
Sadness sounds like a child crying.
Sadness makes me feel heartbroken.

George Flack (8)
Langford Lower School, Langford

In My Element

I am waiting for you
Prowling
In the grass
My fur camouflaging me
And my group
Are all around you
Ready to chase
And dig our sharp teeth
Into your flesh
When I eat you
I can feel the wind
In my fur
I am happy
In my element.

Scott Gulliford (9)
Nant Y Parc Primary School, Senghenydd

Sniper

I am waiting for you
I lie down
In the bright white snow
Sniping down
My prey
The sun gleaming
At lovely tasty prey
I can't wait to
Dig my teeth into your flesh
My prey moves
So I change position
Then I run!
The snow rushes in my face
But soon I fail
I go back to my pack
And wait for you
Then I see my dinner
And snipe again
Then I leap and grab you
I hear you weep and squeak
While I carry you in my jaw
And know we have food tonight!

Jordan Claxton
Nant Y Parc Primary School, Senghenydd

Waiting For You

I am waiting for you
Waiting to run up to you
Fast like a Formula 1 racing car
I am striped like a tiger
My teeth are white and glowing like the sun
I'm waiting to eat
Soon I will run and eat you

I am waiting
In my hole looking for you
I am as fast as a train
Waiting to savage you
To take all your meat and leave only bones
I will suck you till you die!
No one can stop me
I am fast like Usain Bolt
I am waiting for you
So *beware!*
I sleep all day
And search for my prey at night
I will hunt you *down*
Remember! I'm waiting for you!

Bulent Bedir (10)
Nant Y Parc Primary School, Senghenydd

Waiting

I am waiting for you
My teeth shining
Like crystals
It strikes midnight
Pounce up to him
Like a lion
You can hear the footsteps coming

I'm waiting to rip your flesh!
And lick your bones clean
I'm coming closer!
I'll hunt you down
I know where you are
In the dark, deep cave
Remember me
I'll always be there
Hunting you down
You screech when I carry you
To my basement
Caught in my sharp claws
Remember I'll be there.

Nadine Thomas (11)
Nant Y Parc Primary School, Senghenydd

Waiting For You

I am waiting
For my ball
To chew
All day
Like a lion
Eating meat
In the heat
I am waiting for a cat
To chase it away
I love to bounce and pounce
All over you
I want to dig up all the flowers
Like a big digger
I love to go for a run
Like a racing tiger
I lick my lips
When my food comes
I gobble it down
Like a girl rushing her work
I am waiting for you.

Charlotte Moss (9)
Nant Y Parc Primary School, Senghenydd

I'm Waiting For You

I'm waiting for you in the morning
In my burrow
I sleep all day
And dream of you
At night
I hunt you down
I lick my lips
When I know
I am near
The bush
The bush where
You live
You squeal like a pig
When I carry you
In my jaws
Remember me
I am waiting
For you!

Blaze Lewis (10)
Nant Y Parc Primary School, Senghenydd

Waiting For You

I am waiting for you
My sharp, giant claws
Ready to kill
My eyes
Dazzling
Wandering
Around the green jungle
My stomach
Is rumbling
I hear tapping
As the leaves rustle
In the blowing wind
I see you
I hear you
Get ready
I'm going to kill you
Now!

Nicole Gulliford (10)
Nant Y Parc Primary School, Senghenydd

I Am Waiting For You

I am waiting for you
In the deep blue sea
Waiting in my cave
My sparkling fins
Like silver
I am waiting
To dig my teeth
Into your skin
Waiting to get to your
Flesh and blood
I am coming to get you
Remember
I am always waiting.

Jayah Watson (9)
Nant Y Parc Primary School, Senghenydd

Caveman

He's big
He's tough
His voice is rough.

He's mad
He's sad
He's also sometimes bad.

He's mucky
He's yucky
He's also very lucky.

Rowan Harkin (10)
Our Lady's Primary School, Leeds

My Brother

My brother can be kind,
My brother can be sly,
My brother can be mean,
My brother can be shy.

My brother is my twin,
My brother, he loves me.
My brother likes to swim,
He is the best there can be.

Keena Harkin (10)
Our Lady's Primary School, Leeds

Peace

Peace looks like soft pillows.
Peace smells like melted chocolate on a cake.
Peace feels like a soft dove's feathers.
Peace tastes like a fresh peach on a summer's day.
Peace sounds like birds singing happy songs.

Carys Holdsworth (10)
Our Lady's Primary School, Leeds

Anger

Anger looks like the dull cloud on the darkest day.
Anger smells like the rotting wood on a fire.
Anger feels like the thorns on a thorn bush.
Anger tastes like salty seawater.
Anger sounds like the sorrowful souls who have died.

Declan Bingham (10)
Our Lady's Primary School, Leeds

Lizard - Haiku

He lives in a cage
He climbs up and down his branch
All day and through night.

Liam Kirkham (10)
Our Lady's Primary School, Leeds

My House - Haiku

In my lovely house
I always play with my dog
In the afternoon.

Hayden Clarke (10)
Our Lady's Primary School, Leeds

My Grandma's House - Haiku

At my grandma's house
I have my Sunday dinner
When I sleep over.

Kelsey Green (10)
Our Lady's Primary School, Leeds

Anger

Anger is red like a burning fire in a house.
Anger is black like the smoke spreading in the air.
Anger is brown like someone punching you and you get a bruise.
Anger is orange like the colour of fire burning fast.
Anger is pink like you getting tons of warts on your face.

Anger smells like boiling water in a pan making noodles.
Anger smells sweaty like two people fighting.
Anger smells terribly bad like sweaty socks.
Anger smells powerful like God making a flood.
Anger smells extremely bad like rotten eggs out of date.

Anger sounds very loud like drums banging.
Anger sounds extremely noisy like a seagull.
Anger sounds powerfully bad like the Devil destroying the world.
Anger sounds extremely loud like a crow waking you up
                                        in the morning.
Anger sounds dreadful like someone screaming in your ear.

Anger tastes terribly bad like sprouts and onions.
Anger tastes very bad like burned toast on a cold day.
Anger tastes hot like boiling oil in a pan.
Anger tastes like sprouts and cucumber all mixed together.
Anger tastes horrible like mushy peas and potato skins.

Anger looks like fire burning down all the houses.
Anger looks like lava burning down the country.
Anger looks like someone punching you.
Anger looks like someone destroying your car and you
                                        can't stop them.
Anger looks like someone destroying your home for the fun of it.

Anger feels uncontrollable like a boat about to crash.
Anger feels distressing like your dog just got killed by
                                        some teenagers.
Anger feels like you have more energy than a car.
Anger feels like someone parked their car in the middle of the road.

Anger reminds me of fire/lava burning through the town.

Michael Sutherland (10)
Park Primary School, Invergordon

Happiness

Happiness is the colour yellow like the sun coming
out in the morning.
Happiness is the colour blue like the waves in the sea.
Happiness is the colour green like the leaves on the tree
falling to the ground.
Happiness is the colour red like the sun burning.
Happiness is orange like a juicy orange.

Happiness smells like a freshly picked apple.
Happiness smells like an apple pie freshly cooked.
Happiness smells like a cone of chips from the chip shop.
Happiness smells like pink roses in my garden.
Happiness smells like strawberry tart from the baker's.

Happiness sounds like children playing.
Happiness sounds like me on my birthday.
Happiness sounds like me and my friend dancing.
Happiness sounds like me singing.
Happiness sounds like birds singing.

Happiness tastes like a fresh apple pie.
Happiness tastes like melted ice cream.
Happiness tastes like a melted chocolate in your mouth.
Happiness tastes like a cold bottle of juice.
Happiness tastes like hot toast in the morning.

Happiness looks like someone on their wedding day.
Happiness looks like the stars in the sky.
Happiness looks like children playing.
Happiness looks like fun.
Happiness looks like the children playing in the garden.

Happiness feels like writing in my book.
Happiness feels like winning a medal.
Happiness feels like a sweetie in my mouth.
Happiness feels like you're famous.

Happiness reminds me of my family and friends!

Shannon Lyall (10)
Park Primary School, Invergordon

Love

Love is the red colour of people who are in love,
Love is the colour of brown like the sweet chocolate
That you get for your birthday,
Love is like the lovely red rose in the garden,
Love is the colour red like your heart tells you that you're in love,
Love is like the colour blue, like the deep blue sea.

Love smells like the lovely cakes just out of the oven,
Love smells like roses in your garden,
Love smells like the lovely fresh flowers,
Love smells like yummy chocolates,
Love smells like yummy sweets.

Love sounds like the lovely beach,
Love sounds like lovely singing,
Love sounds like the birds flapping their wings,
Love sounds like the lovely masher,
Love sounds like having fun.

Love tastes like lovely chocolate,
Love tastes like lovely juicy fruit,
Love tastes like sweets,
Love tastes like candyfloss,
Love tastes like the fresh air.

Love looks like a kiss on the cheek,
Love looks like a newborn baby,
Love looks like stars in the sky,
Love looks like a tear in your eye,
Love looks like a lovely sunny day.

Love feels like a warm fire,
Love feels like your heart banging 'cause you are in love,
Love feels like you are playing,
Love feels like having a picnic,
Love feels like you are crying.

Love reminds me of a last goodbye.

Sophie Cumming (10)
Park Primary School, Invergordon

Love

Love is red like the first rose just before blossoming.
Love is mellow like the colour yellow.
Love is orange like the juiciest, most colourful orange.
Love is white like the moon in the night.
Love is pink like the bump of a heart.

Love smells like the fresh green grass.
Love smells like a new toy.
Love smells like girls' perfume.
Love smells like a new page.
Love smells like a new life.

Love sounds like the cry of a bird.
Love sounds like the quiet chatter in the class.
Love sounds like the first word of a baby.
Love sounds like a streaming river.
Love sounds like a proposal on a warm day.

Love tastes like a bitter cake.
Love tastes like a wedding cake.
Love tastes like a juicy strawberry.
Love tastes like an oozing pizza.
Love tastes like a hot scone.

Love looks like the new corn.
Love looks like a blossoming rose.
Love looks like a red sky as the sun drifts down.
Love looks like a shining new toy.
Love looks like a newborn calf.

Love feels like a soft hand on your face.
Love feels like the warm sun in your hands.
Love feels like a baby in your arms.
Love feels like the heat of a classroom.

Love reminds me of seeing my brother
For the very first time.

Jordan Ross (10)
Park Primary School, Invergordon

Joy

Joy is the colour red, like fire,
Joy is the colour orange like the sun,
Joy is the colour blue like the wavy sea,
Joy is the colour purple like a happy cartoon character,
Joy is the colour pink like a pretty rose.

Joy smells like some salty sea air,
Joy smells like some fresh-cut grass,
Joy smells like some lovely cooked salmon,
Joy smells like some succulent buttered toast,
Joy smells like some new strawberry candy wrappers.

Joy sounds like the jingle of the ice cream van,
Joy sounds like some toddlers playing,
Joy sounds like an excited crab snapping his claws,
Joy sounds like a funny tune on a children's channel,
Toy sounds like a baby's laugh.

Joy tastes like some sweet candyfloss,
Joy tastes like a chunky chocolate bar,
Joy tastes like some fresh sea food,
Joy tastes like some fresh food at the chippy,
Joy tastes like a lovely takeaway.

Joy looks like little children playing in the sun,
Joy looks like a funny clown making people laugh,
Joy looks like people laughing,
Joy looks like the fiery sun,
Joy looks like the clear blue sky.

Joy feels like the soft fur of a puppy,
Joy feels like the smooth fur of a kitten,
Joy feels like a warm hug,
Joy feels like a cosy bed.

Joy reminds me of happy times in good places.
Joy is amazing!

Graeme Sutherland (10)
Park Primary School, Invergordon

Anger

Anger is red like the fumes of a carton character
Or black like the black eye of a person punching you in a fight.
Anger is green like the grass stain on someone's trousers.
Anger is clear like the teardrops of someone
Or black like the eyesight of someone who has been knocked out.

Anger smells of rubber gloves when being taken into hospital
Or smells of nothing when having a broken nose in a fight.
Anger smells like mud when falling over the root of a tree
Or dew when falling on the grass in the morning.
Anger smells of bark when pushed onto a tree.

Anger sounds like people laughing at you when you fall
Or the sounds of sirens of an ambulance taking you to hospital.
Anger sounds like your parents asking, 'Are you alright, darling?'
Or the beeping of a machine in the hospital keeping you breathing.
Anger sounds like the television in the hollow hospital ward.

Anger tastes of the horrible medicine in hospital
Or pain-breaker tablets trying to ease your pain from the fight.
Anger tastes of bone when being punched in the face.
Anger tastes of blood after being punched in the mouth at night
Or salty tears when crying after being beaten up in a dark alley.

Anger looks like a smirking bully after he or she punched you
Or like grass when tripping over somebody's foot.
Anger looks like a large group of people looking at you
Or like the burning yellow sun making you flinch.
Anger looks like black after being knocked out.

Anger feels like a bony fist hitting you
Or the impact of you falling on the grass,
Or like a nose being broken.
Anger feels like a broken shin.

Anger reminds me of being bullied by someone.

Ryan Duff (10)
Park Primary School, Invergordon

Silence

Silence is yellow like the stars in the sky,
Silence is blue like the blue in my eye,
Silence is green like the leaf on a tree,
Silence is black like the stripes on a bee,
Silence is orange like the sun setting.

Silence smells of the freshly cut grass in my garden,
Silence smells of the freshly baked cakes from my aunty, Mardin,
Silence smells of wood from the floor,
Silence smells of sweets when everyone wants more,
Silence smells of sharpenings just been sharpened from a pencil.

Silence sounds like the rattling from a rattlesnake,
Silence sounds like the baking kit just ready to make,
Silence sounds like the door slamming in my room,
Silence sounds like the drum making a boom,
Silence sounds like the wind whistling in my ear.

Silence tastes like the sweetie melting into a blob,
Silence tastes like the salty tears of a sad person's sob,
Silence tastes like the water running down the hill,
Silence tastes like the dirty taste of a bill,
Silence tastes like roast beef on the table.

Silence looks like the summer sea,
Silence looks like the dark hair on me,
Silence looks like the clouds in the sky,
Silence looks like the TV programme 'Sci Fi',
Silence looks like the newly born puppy.

Silence feels like the smooth pages of a book,
Silence feels like the rubber of where you look,
Silence feels like the cold glass cup,
Silence feels like the warm Christmas sup.

Silence reminds me of a squeaky see-saw.

Ross MacLeod (10)
Park Primary School, Invergordon

Anger

Anger is the black clouds you get in the sky.
Anger is the anger of a cartoon character's face going red.
Anger is like a raging inferno.
Anger is like burning lava in a volcano.
Anger is like a warm fireplace.

Anger smells like burnt sticks on a fire.
Anger smells like vinegar.
Anger smells like smoke from a fire.
Anger smells like burnt toast.
Anger smells like rotten eggs.

Anger sounds like an angry mob.
Anger sounds like a traffic jam.
Anger sounds like a broken car.
Anger sounds like angry children.
Anger sounds like a boat horn.

Anger tastes like smoky air.
Anger tastes like smelly socks.
Anger tastes like old shoelaces.
Anger tastes like old fruit.
Anger tastes like sticky syrup.

Anger looks like a bad sunburn.
Anger looks like a sweating man.
Anger looks like a burnt caravan.
Anger looks like a burning fire.
Anger looks like a dark cloud.

Anger feels like burnt wood.
Anger feels like burnt coal.
Anger feels like a spiky dagger.
Anger feels like hot air coming out of a balloon.

Anger reminds you of a burning fire.

David Majewski (10)
Park Primary School, Invergordon

Silence

Silence is black when you are asleep.
Silence is blue like the sky.
Silence is red when you are angry.
Silence is grey when you are not talking.

Silence smells like the first rose.
Silence smells like the wild flowers growing in your garden.
Silence smells like the new bottle of perfume.
Silence smells like the fresh-cut grass.
Silence smells like the freshly baked pie.

Silence sounds like the calm walk along the beach.
Silence sounds like the calm music.
Silence sounds like the wind brushing against the trees.
Silence sounds like peace.
Silence sounds like the crispy new snow under your feet.

Silence tastes like freshly baked cakes.
Silence tastes like freshly baked tuna.
Silence tastes like the fumes of the vinegar from
                              the fish and chip shop.
Silence tastes like the fumes from the distillery.
Silence tastes like the dinner on the table.

Silence looks like two people not talking.
Silence looks like people arguing.
Silence looks like you are asleep.
Silence looks like the calmness of doing nothing.
Silence looks like a rainy day with nobody outside.

Silence feels like nobody is talking to you.
Silence feels horrible.
Silence feels peaceful.
Silence feels quiet and calm.

Silence reminds me of peace and quiet.

Rebecca Geddes (10)
Park Primary School, Invergordon

Loneliness

Loneliness is black like a lost sheep.
Loneliness is grey like having no friends.
Loneliness is blue like having nothing to do.
Loneliness is red like having no family to talk to.
Loneliness is green like having no shops near your house.

Loneliness smells like hairspray on fire.
Loneliness smells like your house hasn't been cleaned.
Loneliness smells like mould in your house.
Loneliness smells like no windows or doors have been
open for days.
Loneliness smells like sea salt from the beach.

Loneliness sounds like the stars in the sky.
Loneliness sounds like a heart with no beat.
Loneliness sounds like fingers going through your hair.
Loneliness sounds like you're bereaved.
Loneliness sounds like the thunder crashing down when you sit
in the blackness of your house.

Loneliness tastes like a very strong damp taste.
Loneliness tastes like pencil sharpenings in your mouth.
Loneliness tastes like burning.
Loneliness tastes like blood.

Loneliness looks very dark.
Loneliness looks very messy.
Loneliness looks very bossy because it gives you no friends.
Loneliness looks like a dusty window.

Loneliness feels like you want to cry.
Loneliness feels like a bee stinging you.
Loneliness feels like being sick.
Loneliness feels like eating mustard.

Loneliness reminds me of falling out with my friends.

Mollie Mackay
Park Primary School, Invergordon

Silence

Silence is mellow like the colour yellow.
Silence is grey on a gloomy, dark day
Or silence is green like the fresh blowing grass.
Silence is clear like a salty tear.
Silence is blue like the bright sky.

Silence smells of fresh strawberries growing in fields
Or silence smells of new tar down on roads.
Silence smells of roses in gardens.
Silence smells of fresh mint plants
Or silence smells of apples in trees.

Silence sounds like calm music
Or silence sounds like a calm, gentle breeze.
Silence sounds like crackling coal in the fire
Or silence sounds like a calm day.
Silence sounds like apples falling from trees.

Silence tastes like spicy pizza
Or silence tastes like sour lemon.
Silence tastes like ripe oranges.
Silence tastes of warm hot chocolate
Or silence tastes like pure juice.

Silence looks like apples rolling along the ground
Or silence looks like juice dripping from a lemon.
Silence looks like birds flapping their wings
Or silence looks like children running around.
Silence looks like a rabbit jumping around.

Silence feels like squishy dough
Or silence feels like rotten apples.
Silence feels like squishy sweets.
Silence feels quiet and calm.

Silence reminds me of peace and happiness.

Chloe Aikman (10)
Park Primary School, Invergordon

Love

Love is the colour red like a rose.
Love is the colour white like a daisy.
Love is the colour yellow like a melon.
Love is the colour blue like a blueberry.
Love is the colour green like grass.

Love smells of a fresh pie.
Love smells of a flower coming up.
Love smells of freshly cut grass.
Love smells of a fire burning in the winter.
Love smells of lavender as a pillow.

Love sounds like a loaf in the oven.
Love sounds like love of loneliness.
Love sounds like a loaf of bread.
Love sounds like a heart beating so fast.
Love sounds like love hearts beating together.

Love tastes like a sweet for eating.
Love tastes like bread ready for eating.
Love tastes like water being drunk.
Love tastes like ice cream being scooped up.
Love tastes like a hard apple.

Love looks like a heart.
Love looks like a sweet.
Love looks into your heart.
Love looks to someone you love.
Love looks like a rubber.

Love feels like a cake.
Love feels like a banana.
Love feels like an apple.
Love feels like a family loves you and me.

Love reminds me of all the people I love and you.

Bryony Everett (10)
Park Primary School, Invergordon

Fun

Fun is the colour red like a ball.
Fun is the colour pink of a hula hoop.
Fun is the colour green of the grass.
Fun is the colour blue like a card.
Fun is the colour yellow like Lego.

Fun smells of apple pie.
Fun smells like a fish out of the sea.
Fun smells of someone putting perfume on.
Fun smells of someone making pancakes.
Fun smells of someone baking.

Fun sounds like music.
Fun sounds like having fun.
Fun sounds like a horse and its hooves.
Fun sounds like everyone playing.
Fun sounds like everyone having fun in the sand pit.

Fun tastes of a nice sweet.
Fun tastes of fresh grass.
Fun tastes of the nice compost.
Fun tastes of cute dogs.
Fun tastes joyful.

Fun looks like everyone recycling.
Fun looks like someone having a great time.
Fun looks like everyone having fun.
Fun looks like everyone having a good time in school.

Fun feels like a cat licking you.
Fun feels like the air.
Fun feels like a dice.
Fun feels like chalk.

Fun reminds me of a happy day in Glasgow.

Danielle Shields (10)
Park Primary School, Invergordon

Silence

Silence is clear like the salty teardrops
Falling from your eyes when you cry.
Silence is blue like the bright sea
On a calm but sunny day.
Silence is pink like the beautiful lilies
Slowly rocking back and forth in the wind.
Silence is white like a blank piece of paper
Sitting on a table.
Silence is green like the wind
Slowly making its way through the grass.
Silence smells like the beautiful wild flowers
Slowly growing in your garden.
Silence smells of a freshly made cake
Sitting in a bakery's window.
Silence smells of the salt water
As you sit down to have a picnic on the beach.
Silence smells of the sweet blossom
As it grows on the tree outside your garden.
Silence smells of car fumes
As it quickly passes by.
Silence sounds like a beautiful butterfly's wings
Gently banging together to make it fly.
Silence sounds like a leaf
Slowly falling to the ground.
Silence sounds like the bright sun
Going down behind the hills.
Silence sounds like the clouds
Gently moving to the west.
Silence sounds like a person sleeping.
Silence tastes like a thick, creamy cake
In the morning.

Tayllur Mackenzie (10)
Park Primary School, Invergordon

Silence

Silence is yellow like the sun shining down,
Silence is clear because it's blank,
Silence is black like the doom's hole,
Silence is purple like the sunset over the hill,
Silence is red like a heart.

Silence smells of fresh pie sitting in the window,
Silence smells like the vinegary chips in the chip shop,
Silence smells like the blossomed roses in the garden,
Silence smells like the tyres skidding on the race cars,
Silence smells like new tar.

Silence sounds like no sound at all,
Silence sounds like birds in the morning,
Silence sounds like the horns of the ships leaving Invergordon,
Silence sounds like the loud exhausts of cars,
Silence sounds like the music at church on Sundays.

Silence tastes like bacon for breakfast,
Silence tastes like runny custard at night,
Silence tastes like thick semolina,
Silence tastes like spaghetti,
Silence tastes like stewed sausages.

Silence looks like a snowy day,
Silence looks like a bin blowing away,
Silence looks like a blizzard,
Silence looks like a car being blown from side to side,
Silence looks like a big bridge.

Silence feels like a bubble inside your stomach,
Silence feels like a vibration on the ground,
Silence feels like a hot feeling on your hand.

Robert Mackenzie (10)
Park Primary School, Invergordon

Silence

Silence is blue like the sky above us all.
Silence is white like a clear, blank page
Or green like the fresh summer's grass.
Silence is clear just like a tear
Or black like a stray cat.

Silence smells of fresh, new summer roses.
Silence smells of newly cut grass
Or fresh air blowing through your hair.
Silence smells of perfume flying around the air.
Silence smells of new flowers popping up from the ground.

Silence sounds like a hummingbird humming around at sunset.
Silence sounds like music in your ears
Or wind blowing through the tree.
Silence sounds like peace and quiet.
Silence sounds like a cute puppy's bark.

Silence tastes like fresh air blowing around.
Silence tastes like a mouth-watering pizza or nice fresh cake.
Silence tastes like friendship.

Silence looks like a clear summer's day.
Silence looks like a fresh morning or a dark night.
Silence looks like a fresh, new meal.
Silence looks like a new day.

Silence feels like soft fur on a puppy's back.
Silence feels like wind through your fingers.
Silence feels like a calm, gentle breeze on your face.
Silence feels like a puppy licking your hand.

Silence reminds me of a cute, gentle puppy.

Bethany Bremner (9)
Park Primary School, Invergordon

Happiness!

Happiness is yellow like joy and mellow.
Happiness is pink like the smell of fresh perfume.
Happiness is green for go.
Happiness is purple like a tulip in a field.
Happiness is white like the first drops of snow.

Happiness smells like freshly cut grass.
Happiness smells like the sweetest rose.
Happiness smells like the best perfume.
Happiness smells like a freshly baked pie.
Happiness smells like the fresh air in your hair.

Happiness sounds like children laughing and playing.
Happiness sounds like a bubble machine bubbling.
Happiness sounds like a CD player at its highest volume.
Happiness sounds like children's feet.
Happiness sounds like children screaming with joy.

Happiness feels like catching a soft ball.
Happiness feels like a big, warm hug.
Happiness feels like the air going through your hair.
Happiness feels like happiness.

Happiness tastes like sweeties.
Happiness tastes like a baked cake.
Happiness tastes like a pizza with extra toppings.
Happiness tastes like a freshly baked pie.
Happiness tastes like doughnuts, mmm . . .

Happiness reminds me of last Christmas!

Millie Flynn (9)
Park Primary School, Invergordon

Silence

The colour of silence is blue because of the calm sea,
The colour of silence is green because of the grass,
The colour of silence is yellow because it's mellow,
The colour of silence is white because of blank paper.

The smell of silence is fresh air blowing,
The smell of silence is bread just made,
The smell of silence is roses in the morning,
The smell of silence is fresh cut grass,
The smell of silence is the ground just dug up.

The sound of silence is nothing,
The sound of silence is the birds singing in the morning,
The sound of silence is listening to calm music,
The sound of silence is a calm and quiet day fishing.

Silence tastes of fresh bread just made,
Silence tastes of a nice juicy apple,
Silence tastes of fresh cut grass,
Silence tastes of fresh air blowing in the wind.

Silence looks like a nice relaxing day out in the sun,
Silence looks like the sun is never going to end,
Silence looks like a nice relaxing time on a boat,
Silence looks like a nice time.

Silence reminds you of a nice day
That's never going to end.

David Shivas (10)
Park Primary School, Invergordon

Silence

Silence is yellow like the sun in the sky.
Silence is green like the grass.
Silence is white like the moon.

Silence smells like chips.
Silence smells like fresh air.
Silence smells like chocolate.

Silence sounds like air.
Silence sounds like a zip.
Silence sounds like a boot.

Silence tastes like food.
Silence tastes like fresh water.
Silence tastes like fresh beef.

Silence looks like a book.
Silence looks like a kit.
Silence looks like a box.

Silence feels like grass.
Silence feels like books.
Silence feels like a star.

Silence reminds you of the fresh air.

Connor Black (10)
Park Primary School, Invergordon

Joy

Joy is blue like a bird in the sky.
Joy is blue like a bottle.
Joy is blue like the ocean.

Joy smells like chips in the café.
Joy smells like fire from a bonfire.
Joy smells like the fresh air.

Joy sounds like planes passing by.
Joy sounds like cars going past.
Joy sounds like the sea washing in.

Joy tastes like fish from the sea.
Joy tastes like bacon from a pig.
Joy tastes like tuna pasta.

Joy looks like streetlights in the town.
Joy looks like bins in school.
Joy looks like clocks on the wall.

Joy feels like a front window.
Joy feels like a bus.
Joy feels like a piece of wood.

Brandon Stone (10)
Park Primary School, Invergordon

River Bollin

The river is a never-ending stream of blue shades,
The river is as calm as sun rising in the sky,
The river is as quiet as a mouse in a dark hole,
The river is as pretty as a butterfly on a flower,
The river is a racing hound trying to catch its prey,
The river is as blue as the sky on a sunny day,
The sun beams on the meandering River Bollin,
The River Bollin shimmers like stars at night
And that's why we love it.

Sophie McFarlane (11)
Prestbury CE Primary School, Macclesfield

The River Bollin

It begins as a child
As everything will
A hope, a dream
A need to fulfil.

At first a trickle
Wiry and thin
The power to forgive
To cleanse all sin.

Tributaries arrive
Greeted as old friends
To join it with its journey
Through twists and bends.

A bridge stands dominant
Like a gateway
Its foundations lie deep in water
Where the rocks lay.

Through town and country
It meanders on
Towards the seafront
Its adventure is almost done.

With evening on its fingertips
It gives in to the flow
It relents to a calm gush
Lets its strongholds go.

The day has ended
Nobody around
It waits for the morning
For the morning's sound.

Megan Smith (11)
Prestbury CE Primary School, Macclesfield

River Bollin Poem

Rushing, racing,
Flowing speedily along the quiet riverbanks,
Shimmering in the sunlight,
Dancing in the moonlight,
It shines like a star in the dark night sky.
As it meanders backwards and forwards
It is a never-ending blue road.
It is a wild dog chasing its prey across the savannah,
The banks are surrounded by curious wildlife.
The trees sway gently in the wind.

Daisy Chaplin (11) & Eleanor Newsome (11)
Prestbury CE Primary School, Macclesfield

Love

Love is red like my big beating heart.
Love is white like the fur of a kitten.
Love reminds me of being tickled with the feather of a dove.
Love reminds me of being proud of my work.
Love feels like a warm fur coat in the cold winter.
Love feels like a small beagle puppy sleeping on your lap.
Love tastes sweet like chocolate truffles touching your tongue.
Love tastes like the juiciest plum from the tree.
Love smells like the rose from the heart.
Love is blue like the bright morning sky.
Love reminds me of a field of daffodils.
Love looks like the beautiful starry night sky.
Love is life!

Ami Hope (10)
Roseberry Primary School, Billingham

Love

Love is white like a beautiful, gracious dove.
Love is red like a blooming rose.
Love is like a small fluffy dog.
Love is warm like the sun.
Love is like a gentle hug from a friend.
Love is like a soft fluffy pillow.
Love tastes like strawberries.
Love smells like freshly melted chocolate.
Love tastes like ice cream on a hot summer's day.
Love smells like a newborn rose.
Love looks like an old couple on the beach.
Love looks like a beating heart in front of a couple.

Amie Salmon (10)
Roseberry Primary School, Billingham

Love

Love is red like a blood-red rose.
Love is warm like a soft, delicate blanket.
Love is family or a great warm hug.
Love is soft like the soft, fragile snow.
Love calls for friendship and family.
Love is ripe like the strawberry ready for eating.
Love can help illness or wounds.
Love is soft like a baby's bottom.
Love is life like my mum's heart, loving and caring.
Love can help people be one part.
Love can do a favour or two.
Love is a shield like a locked door keeping certain things out.

Bethany Parsons (11)
Roseberry Primary School, Billingham

Fear

Fear is black like the dark alley at night.
Fear is white like the glowing outline of a ghost.

Fear rumbles like the loud, deadly sound of thunder.
Fear screams like a terrified woman calling for help.

Fear is sickening like the awful taste of Brussels sprouts.
Fear is gruesome like broccoli on my plate.

Fear is the smell of the salty sea where sharks lurk.
Fear is the smell of stomach-churning petrol.

Fear is the silky feeling of a smooth cobweb.
Fear feels wobbly like my legs on a high cliff.

Chloe Dixon (10)
Roseberry Primary School, Billingham

Fun

Fun is yellow like the sun shining over me.
Fun is pink like my bedroom walls.

Fun sounds like laughter of children in the playground.
Fun sounds like the tapping of my shoes.

Fun smells like the flowers in my garden.
Fun smells like the fruit in my yoghurt.

Fun feels like swimming in a pool of chocolate.
Fun feels like sliding down a rainbow.

Fun tastes of cold ice cream.
Fun tastes like the sweet scent of roses.

Maime McCorkell (11)
Roseberry Primary School, Billingham

Silence

Silence is grey like a storm cloud.
Silence is black like the sky at night.
Silence is like loneliness forever.
Silence is like being in your own world.
Silence is like a horrible big web.
Silence is like a cold, lonely room.
Silence smells like salt in a quiet sea.
Silence smells like cold in a park.
Silence tastes like a sour pea.
Silence tastes like bad chicken.
This is what silence is like.

Kye Ayre (10)
Roseberry Primary School, Billingham

Love

Love is red like a thousand hearts.
Love is like your life going on and on for ever and ever.
Love feels like a comfy blanket keeping me warm.
Love is pink like a newborn baby piglet.
Love is like an old couple holding hands on a beautiful sandy beach.
Love feels like a cute newborn baby in their mum's hands
getting cuddles.
Love is like a happy couple getting married.
Love is white like a blanket of soft, smooth snow.
Love feels like a comfy blanket.
That is love.

Selina Royal (10)
Roseberry Primary School, Billingham

Fear

Fear is salty blue, where the sharks lurk in the sea.
Fear is black like the dark street at night.
Fear is brown like spiders clinging to the wall.
Fear is green like the taste of cucumber.

Fear sounds like the scream of death.
Fear sounds like the creak of an ancient oak door.
Fear sounds like the ghostly voice in an old house.

Fear is the revolting taste of blood.
Fear is the smell of gas.
Fear is the touch of cobwebs.

Chloe Umpleby (10)
Roseberry Primary School, Billingham

Fear

Fear is white like the sharp, deadly teeth of a shark.
Fear is brown like the horrible sickly taste of mushrooms.
Fear is yellow like the sharp flickers of lightning.

Fear howls like the threatening sound of a whimpering ghost.
Fear roars like the extraordinary sound of a hungry lion.

Fear is gruesome like brown, long, minced meat.
Fear is sickening like the gut-wrenching taste of sprouts.

Fear is the feel of wet, sticky, wobbly jelly.
Fear is the feel of a smooth cobweb.

Tara Conway (10)
Roseberry Primary School, Billingham

Happiness

Happiness is yellow like the big smiley face of the sun.
Happiness is white like a big empty space of nothing.
Happiness is like going to your favourite place.
Happiness feels like a puppy sitting on your knee.
Happiness feels like a bouncy ball bouncing across the floor.
Happiness looks like my happy, cuddly teddies huddled together.
Happiness tastes like a giant ice cream.
Happiness tastes like a chocolate cake.
Happiness smells like blooming flowers.
Happiness smells like my mum's cooking.

Amy Whitehouse (10)
Roseberry Primary School, Billingham

Anger

Anger is red like blood in my body.
Anger is black like ink in my pen.
Anger is like a big grey cloud.
Anger smells like rotten eggs.
Anger tastes like sour sweets.
Anger feels like a firework going off.
Anger reminds me of my nanna shouting.
Anger feels like teeth grinding.
Anger is dark like shadows.
Anger is like a frying pan bubbling over.

Danni Evans (11)
Roseberry Primary School, Billingham

Happiness

Happiness is yellow like a warm sun with a small breeze.
Happiness is blue like the morning sky and the calming sea.
Happiness is like winning a race.
Happiness is like being with friends and family.
Happiness is like a newborn puppy, safe and warm.
Happiness is like a soft, fluffy blanket.
Happiness tastes like sweet candyfloss at a theme park.
Happiness smells like freshly made cakes.
Happiness looks like a box of chocolates.

Olivia Teague (10)
Roseberry Primary School, Billingham

Love Is . . .

Love is brown like my pet hamster.
Love sounds comforting like my mum's voice.
Love tastes lovely, like the creaminess of Nutella.
Love smells sweet like the scent of my home.
Love feels soft like the cover of my bed.

Samantha Burns (10)
Roseberry Primary School, Billingham

Fun

Fun is red like the Blackpool Tower.
Fun is blue like the colour of the water in the swimming pool.
Fun is yellow like the stripes on the picnic blanket.
Fun is white like the colour of the shopping bags.

Fun is noisy like the elevators in the tower.
Fun is calm like the sound of water.
Fun is crackly like the sounds of the picnic blanket.
Fun is rattley like the sound of my shopping bag.

Hollie Robinson (10)
Roseberry Primary School, Billingham

Happiness

Happiness is red like a big bright smile.
Happiness is yellow like the sun.
Happiness reminds me of a cute little puppy.
Happiness reminds me of a big bright star.
Happiness looks like a great big bouncy ball.
Happiness looks like a teddy bear.
Happiness feels like a quilt cover.
Happiness feels like a sunny day.

Sasha Kane (10)
Roseberry Primary School, Billingham

Jealousy

Jealousy is white and rusty and old
Like my horrible cousin's motorhome.

Jealousy is black and silver
Like my mam's extreme and super-fast laptop.

Jealousy is black and white
Like my auntie and uncle's
Delicate, clean and immaculate wedding.

Morgan Harvey (10)
Roseberry Primary School, Billingham

Fun Is . . .

Fun is a hound darting faster and faster.
Fun is a furnace fire, red but still yellow.
Fun smells like mud and a plate of joy or chips.
Fun is a drink of Coke at Christmas.
Fun is brilliant.
Fun tastes like a home-made dinner
With an English Yorkshire pudding.
Fun is excellent.

James Wharton (10)
Roseberry Primary School, Billingham

Happiness

Happiness is red like a lovely red carpet.
Happiness is blue like a beautiful sky.
Happiness is pink like a smelly sock.
Happiness is like a walk in the park.
Happiness is like a dream that never ends.
Happiness is like a baby and its mother.
Happiness is like a blanket, fluffy and safe.
Happiness is like toys, soft, and keeps me warm.

Kira Michaelson (10)
Roseberry Primary School, Billingham

Fun

Fun is green like a football pitch.
Fun is brown like the trees I climb.
Fun is the laugh of a little girl.
Fun is the screams of kids on a roller coaster.
Fun is the talk of happy kids.
Fun tastes like apple in the crumble.
Fun tastes like custard on a jam roly-poly.
Fun smells like jam in a roly-poly.

Alisha Norton (10)
Roseberry Primary School, Billingham

Fun

Fun is blue like the swaying water in the pool.
Fun is pink like the time I meet my friends.
Fun is brown like the colour of my fluffy dog.

Fun sounds like the screaming of children on the playground.
Fun tastes like a big, giant, candyfloss.
Fun smells like the fish and chip shop.
Fun feels like the sponge in the bath.

Megan Carter (10)
Roseberry Primary School, Billingham

Fun

Fun is bright like my football strip.
Fun is laughter when the comedian tells a joke.
Fun is like marvellous chewing gum and
I always have the taste in my mouth.
Fun has that great smell of the fresh green grass when I play football.
Fun has a feeling like when you score a goal
And you have that buzz.

Morgan Guest (10)
Roseberry Primary School, Billingham

Silence

Silence is snow white for there is nothing there.
Silence can be pitch-black and start to give you a scare.

Silence is creepy because it seems to scream.
Silence is like people locked in some chains.

Silence feels like it's grabbing your arm.
Silence feels lonely and sad because no one is quiet.

Rebecca Porritt (11)
Roseberry Primary School, Billingham

Sadness Is . . .

Sadness is black like a widow's dress.
Sadness is white like the skin of a dead relative.

Sadness sounds like the slammed door of my brother walking in.
Sadness sounds like the whines of the poor dog.
Sadness sounds like the cries of death.

Sadness tastes like the drippiness of tears.

Sean Ellison (10)
Roseberry Primary School, Billingham

Happiness

Happiness is yellow like a big sunflower.
Happiness is orange like the sun in the sky.

Happiness feels like joy.
Happiness is like bouncing bunnies in a field.

Happiness is like the best thing ever.
Happiness is like smiling and smiling forever.

Chloe Bradley (10)
Roseberry Primary School, Billingham

Anger

Anger is as red as my teacher's pen.
Anger is as red as my blood.
Anger reminds me of shouting.
Anger reminds me of stressing out.
Anger feels like stones hitting windows.
Anger feels like a football hitting the back of the net.

Antony Beedle (10)
Roseberry Primary School, Billingham

Terror

Terror is like black blindness
And like ghosts in a corridor.
Terror feels like a stranger
Strangling you in a dark alleyway.
Terror smells like dead bodies
Rotting with maggots squirming.

Lee Russell (10)
Roseberry Primary School, Billingham

Love

Love is gold like a golden ring going on forever.
Love is pink like a big fragrant rose.
Love reminds me of a walk to the end of the world.
Love reminds me of a happiness that lasts for ever and ever.
Love feels like a fluffy blanket keeping me warm.
Love feels like a family keeping warm at Christmas.

Chris Atkin (10)
Roseberry Primary School, Billingham

Fun!

Fun is silver like the disco ball above the dance floor.
Fun sounds like the screaming of the children on the roller coaster.
Fun smells fresh like the air surrounding the playground.
Fun feels smooth like the keys on the black laptop!
Fun tastes sweet like the giant, round, lollipop.

Sarah Bauckham (10)
Roseberry Primary School, Billingham

Love

Love is gold like my mam's lipstick.
Love is like my mam's voice when she is singing.
Love is chocolate cake that she sometimes makes.
Love is like 'Kate Moss', my mam's favourite perfume.
Love is my mam's warm hugs.

Courtney Shannon (10)
Roseberry Primary School, Billingham

Fun

Fun is blue when I go swimming.
Fun is laughter, like in the park.
Fun is ice cream on a hot sunny day.
Fun is like fish and chips on the beach.
Fun feels like the soft towel when I get out of the sea.

Liana Keaveney (10)
Roseberry Primary School, Billingham

Pain

Pain is red like blood coming from your eyes
Pain is black like an alleyway without any lights
Pain is like walking on the street alone and afraid
Pain is like falling down and down forever
Pain is like loneliness and fear
Pain is like broken glass in your head.

Daniel Brooks (10)
Roseberry Primary School, Billingham

My Hobbies

My favourite hobby is gymnastics,
I love doing kicks and flicks.

When I jump very high,
I go into the sky.

I come back very fast,
I never come last.

I have more hobbies, like dancing,
I do a spin like I have wings.

I love the noise of my tap shoes,
When I come home I never want to snooze.

I do the flute, I really, really love it,
I sometimes sit, I sometimes stand.

I do it with my music teacher,
I thought she was a creature,
She reminds me of mice

I love all my hobbies
And I especially like lollies.

I've got to go, I will say goodbye,
So let's all go and have a pie.

Annie Krantz (9)
Swinderby All Saints Primary School, Lincoln

My Secret Place

I have a secret place just for me,
It's a place where I can be free.
It's my secret place just for me,
It's a place where I am free.

It isn't high up in the sky,
Where the birds fly silently by.
It isn't hidden down below
Inside a fox's treacherous burrow.

I have a secret place just for me,
It's a place where I can be free.

It isn't where the mountains are
Or in the deep blue ocean swirling far.
It isn't in the pine forest
Where the smell is simply bliss.

I have a secret place just for me,
It's a place where I can be free.

My secret place is when I'm asleep,
I dream of everything, including the beach.
Endless possibilities fill my mind,
My secret place is in my mind.

Thomas Osborne-Day (9)
Swinderby All Saints Primary School, Lincoln

The Magic Box

(Based on 'Magic Box' by Kit Wright)

I will put in my box . . .
The *grrr* of a lion's roar
And the shriek of a super, scary skeleton
And the roar of the wild waves on a wet, windy night.

I will put in my box . . .
Three black shadows spoken in German,
The last flash of lightning
And the first buzz of a busy bumblebee.

I will put in my box . . .
The ninth wonder of the world,
A blue pig and a black sun,
A horse in the desert and a camel in a stable.

My box is constructed from bones and brains and blood,
With spiders' legs on the lid and cobwebs in the corners.
Its hinges are the wings of a swan.

I will dive in my box
Under the huge and powerful Niagara Falls,
Then dive into the Atlantic
The colour of ice.

Elizabeth McIntyre (9)
Thurston CE (VC) Primary School, Bury St Edmunds

The Magic Box

(Based on 'Magic Box' by Kit Wright)

I will put in my box . . .
The gentle rustle of a weak, wet wind.

I will put in my box . . .
Three crazy, colourful clouds seen in France,
The last tooth left in an ancient child's mouth
And the first balloon popped at a party.

I will put in my box . . .
A second sun and a purple deer,
A baby on a horse
And a warrior on a kitten.

My box is designed from twigs and leaves and grass,
With snow on the lid and wishes in the corners.
Its hinges are the jawbones of a human.

I will swim in my box
Across the calm, warm, gentle River Nile,
Then sit upon a warm, sandy beach
On a tropical island near Egypt,
The colour of a turned-on lamp.

Abbie Cook (8)
Thurston CE (VC) Primary School, Bury St Edmunds

The Magic Box

(Based on 'Magic Box' by Kit Wright)

I will put in my box . . .
The winds whistling at the wild waves
And the rustling leaves
Crackling in the bright autumn sun.

I will put in my box . . .
Three golden eggs whispered in German,
The last chuckle of a cheeky chimp
And the first clatter from a chipped tooth.

I will put in my box . . .
The ninth tentacle of an octopus and a black skeleton,
Water in a house and a sofa in a swimming pool.

My box is designed from rubber and plastic and fabric,
With flowers on the lid and fish-eyes in the corners.
Its hinges are the wings of a sparrow.

I will sail in my box
Across the calm, warm waves of the Indian Ocean,
Then dock at a rocky harbour,
The colour of a silver watch.

Olivia Stevens (8)
Thurston CE (VC) Primary School, Bury St Edmunds

The Magic Box

(Based on 'Magic Box' by Kit Wright)

I will put in my box . . .
A tortoise from Turkey torturing a tiger,
A sleeping, slithery, slimy snake curled round in a swirl.

I will put in my box . . .
Three turquoise turtles told in Turkish,
The last mumble from a huge hippo
And the first splash from a pond.

I will put in my box . . .
The sixteenth leg from a jelly fish
And a purple piece of sweetcorn,
A parrot in a house an a person in a cage.

My box is designed from glass and plastic and wood,
With stars on the lid and bees in the corners.
Its hinges are the blades of scissors.

I will ride my bike in my box
Across the gentle and warm Red Sea,
Then I will ride across a dark tropical island
The colour of turquoise.

Sarah Castle (8)
Thurston CE (VC) Primary School, Bury St Edmunds

The Magic Box

(Based on 'Magic Box' by Kit Wright)

I will put in my box . . .
The roar of the rocks on the cliff
Crashing to the floor.

I will put in my box . . .
Three turquoise spotted tigers yelling in Turkish,
The last kick of a football
And the first hit of a tiny tennis ball.

I will put in my box . . .
A second universe and a purple sky,
A knight on a cow and a swimmer in a rocket.

My box is assembled from blackberries,
Strawberries and raspberries,
With ghosts on the lid and zombies in the corners.
Its hinges are the jawbones of a python.

I will windsurf in my box over the small,
Lappy Caribbean Ocean,
Then arrive on a Caribbean island
The colour of bananas.

Jamie Dempsey (8)
Thurston CE (VC) Primary School, Bury St Edmunds

The Magic Box

(Based on 'Magic Box' by Kit Wright)

I will put in my box . . .
The crackle of the crazy, crushed Coco Pops
And the pop of a purple and pink party balloon.

I will put in my box . . .
Three cerise prayers screamed in Swedish,
The last piece of chocolate from a shop
And the first neigh of a baby foal.

I will put in my box . . .
The ninth wonder of the world and a pink leaf,
A chimp in a house and a person in a cage.

My box is designed from diamonds, rubies and amethysts,
With horseshoes on the lid
And baby monkeys in the corners.
Its hinges are the tailbone of a dog.

I will ride my horse in my box
Through the green gooey water of a garden pond,
Then arrive in a field of four-foot long grass,
The colour of a green pond.

Caitlan Cox (8)
Thurston CE (VC) Primary School, Bury St Edmunds

The Magic Box

(Based on 'Magic Box' by Kit Wright)

I will put in my box . . .
The sound of a lion's roar
And the shriek of a super-scary skeleton,
And the roar of the wild waves on a wet Wednesday.

I will put in my box . . .
Three black shadows shouting in German,
The last crown of an ancient king
And the first buzz of a busy bumblebee.

I will put in my box . . .
A red planet and a blue raccoon,
A cat on a lead and a dog chasing a butterfly.

My box is designed from a cobra's skin, a hedgehog's spine
And a rabbit's skull,
With spiders' legs on the lid and cobwebs in the corners.
Its hinges are the eyes of a spider.

I will kite-surf in my box
Under the huge and powerful Niagara Falls,
Then crash on the white beaches of North Fiji.

Adam Ryan-Self (9)
Thurston CE (VC) Primary School, Bury St Edmunds

The Magic Box

(Based on 'Magic Box' by Kit Wright)

I will put in my box . . .
The winds whistling at the waves
And rustling leaves crackling
In the bright autumn sun.

I will put in my box . . .
Three ruby rainbows said in Spanish,
The last toffee apple from an ancient child
And the first leap of a leopard.

I will put in my box . . .
The fifth leg of a cat and some pink grass,
And a human in a nest and a bird in a house.

My box is designed from rubies and crystals and diamonds,
With hearts on the lid and icicles in the corners.
Its hinges are the wings of a blue tit.

I will water ski in my box
Across the warm, gentle, Pacific Ocean
Then arrive at the beach in Alcudia,
The colour of blue and yellow.

Zara Doman (8)
Thurston CE (VC) Primary School, Bury St Edmunds

The Magic Box

(Based on 'Magic Box' by Kit Wright)

I will put in my box . . .
The roar in the rain on the red Russian racing car.

I will put in my box . . .
Three silver suns shrieked in Spanish,
The last apple from a tall tree
And the first fright of a funny zombie.

I will put in my box . . .
A purple poppy,
A moon in the day
And a sun in the night.

My box is constructed from rubies and bananas and peanuts,
With eyeballs on the lid and stink bombs in the corners.
Its hinges are the jawbones of a blue whale.

I will waterski in my box
Over the massive, deep waters of the Pacific Ocean,
Then crack my ski on the rock-hard pebbles of a Mexican beach
The colour of smoke.

Adam Levey (8)
Thurston CE (VC) Primary School, Bury St Edmunds

The Magic Box

(Based on 'Magic Box' by Kit Wright)

I will put in my box . . .
The crash of the waves on the ragged rocks.

I will windsurf in my box
On the North Atlantic Ocean
On the stormy sea,
Then land on a hot, stony beach
In North America,
The colour of black.

Adam Sage (8)
Thurston CE (VC) Primary School, Bury St Edmunds

The Magic Box

(Based on 'Magic Box' by Kit Wright)

I will put in my box . . .
The crackling of a fire
And the silver, shimmering shine of a sword.

I will put in my box . . .
Three bright purple-yellow stars whispered in Maltese,
The last blossom on the tree
And the first laugh of a hungry hyena.

I will put in my box . . .
A tenth planet and a pink daffodil,
And a dolphin on a ladybird.

My box is designed from chocolate and toffees and cherries,
With emeralds on the lid and diamonds in the corners.
Its hinges are the leg joints of a frog.

I will windsurf in my box
On the gentle Caribbean waves
Then land on Aldburgh beach
The colour of golden yellow sand.

Millie Talbot (8)
Thurston CE (VC) Primary School, Bury St Edmunds

The Magic Box

(Based on 'Magic Box' by Kit Wright)

I will put in my box . . .
The gentle rustle of a weak, wet wind.

I will put in my box . . .
Three crazy, colourful clouds seen in France,
The last tooth left in an ancient child's mouth
And the first balloon popped at a party.

I will put in my box . . .
A fifth wheel of a car and the pink tip of a tiger's tail,
A squirrel in a school
And a human in a tree.

My box is constructed from books and paper and fabric
With snowmen on the lid and stones in the corners.
Its hinges are the pincers of a crab.

I will go kayaking in my box
On the calm shine of the English Channel,
Then overturn on the beautiful beach of Sungat,
The colour of the browny beach.

Jessica Hodson (8)
Thurston CE (VC) Primary School, Bury St Edmunds

The Magic Box

(Based on 'Magic Box' by Kit Wright)

I will put in my box . . .
The snooziest snore of the sleepiest, scariest
Slithering snake.

I will put in my box . . .
Three smells of an ice cream told in Hungarian,
The last leaf from a tree
And the first conker from a chestnut tree.

I will put in my box . . .
The 25th hour of the day and a purple sea,
A conker on an oak tree and an acorn on a chestnut tree.

My box is constructed from bones and bronze and crystal,
With rubies on the lid and blood in the corners.
Its hinges are the kneecaps of a skeleton.

I will swim in my box across the warm, deep, blue
Parts of the English Channel,
Then come ashore at Cromer, warm and sunny,
The colour of light.

Robbie Pointer (8)
Thurston CE (VC) Primary School, Bury St Edmunds

The Magic Box

(Based on 'Magic Box' by Kit Wright)

I will put in my box . . .
The roar of a red racing car.

I will put in my box . . .
Three golden prayers screeched in Italian,
The last win of Michael Schumacher
And the first big bang of a big bomb.

I will put in my box . . .
An eighth continent and a golden star,
The moon in the day
And the sun in the night.

My box is built from coal and slate and stone,
With nuts on the lid and jokes in the corners.
Its hinges are the elbow joints of a man.

I will cruise in my box
Across the rough waves of the Pacific Ocean,
Then dock at a sunny North American port
The colour of shiny silver.

Nathan Wallace (8)
Thurston CE (VC) Primary School, Bury St Edmunds

The Magic Box

(Based on 'Magic Box' by Kit Wright)

I will put in my box . . .
The bang of a big gun,
The dark demon with red eyes
And a spark from a deadly skeleton.

I will put in my box . . .
Three golden armies shouting in alien,
The last battle of D-Day
And the first born chipmunk.

I will put in my box . . .
A three-eyed owl and a black sun
And an elephant on a turtle.

My box is crafted from skulls and gold and rubies,
With skulls on the lid and rubies in the corners.
Its hinges are the wings of a pterodactyl.

I will kite-surf on my box
Across the River Nile in the huge and powerful winds,
And arrive at warm and sandy Florida.

Josh Whiting (8)
Thurston CE (VC) Primary School, Bury St Edmunds

The Magic Box

(Based on 'Magic Box' by Kit Wright)

I will put in my box . . .
The snooziest snore of the sleepiest, scariest snake.

I will put in my box . . .
Three icy, white ice creams shouting in Swedish,
The last mammoth footprint in history
And the first fireman in his red fire engine.

I will put in my box . . .
The 25th hour of the day and a red moon,
A duck in a car and a person in a lake.

My box is designed from chocolate and toffees and caramel,
With frost on the lid and snow in the corners.
Its hinges are the jaws of a girl.

I will water ski in my box
On the smooth, hot Caribbean Sea,
Then water ski to a perfect Caribbean island
The colour of a pineapple smoothie.

Eloise Richardson (8)
Thurston CE (VC) Primary School, Bury St Edmunds

The Magic Box

(Based on 'Magic Box' by Kit Wright)

I will put in my box . . .
The roar of a lion.

I will put in my box . . .
Three golden bars shouted in Portuguese,
The last song of a concert
And the first laugh of a hungry hyena.

I will put in my box . . .
A third ear and a pink snowman
And a dolphin on a surfboard.

My box is fashioned from gold and rocks and pearls
With glass on the lid and bronze in the corners.
Its hinges are like the wings of an eagle flapping.

I will kite-surf in my box
On the black, deep water.
I will end in a jungle so hot,
Where the sea is turquoise and the leaves are green.

Kieron Frost (8)
Thurston CE (VC) Primary School, Bury St Edmunds

The Magic Box

(Based on 'Magic Box' by Kit Wright)

I will put in my box . . .
The crash of the waves onto the rough sea.

I will put in my box . . .
Three golden armies speaking in Spanish,
The last person living on Earth
And the first hit of a small tennis ball.

I will put in my box . . .
A second head and a pink sun
And a dog driving a car.

My box is assembled from coal and slate and stone,
With eagles on the lid and raindrops in the corners.
Its hinges are the kneecaps of a skeleton.

I will windsurf in my box
On the roaring red, warm sea,
Then land on a sandy beach in Hunstanton,
The colour of blue.

Kieran Hutchens (8)
Thurston CE (VC) Primary School, Bury St Edmunds

The Magic Box

(Based on 'Magic Box' by Kit Wright)

I will put in my box . . .
The crackle of the crispy Coco Pops.

I will put in my box . . .
A snake with one leg and a blue skin
And a pig with horseshoes.

I will put in my box . . .
Three roars from an engine in Egypt,
The last flash of lightning
And the first sense of smell.

My box is designed from crystals and diamonds and iron,
With flesh on the lid and blood in the corners.
Its hinges are the tongues of robins.

I will go canoeing in my box
On the calm River Nile,
Then land off the Caribbean,
The colour of crystal-clear water.

Eddie Allen (8)
Thurston CE (VC) Primary School, Bury St Edmunds

The Magic Box

(Based on 'Magic Box' by Kit Wright)

I will put in my box . . .
The sound of a door slamming
In the morning at 6 o'clock.

I will put in my box . . .
Three gleaming turquoise worlds
Screaming in Russian,
The last pot from ancient Greece
And the first tooth of a baby.

My box is constructed from diamonds
And rubies and crystals,
With kneecaps on the lid and stomachs in the corners.
It's hinges are the legs of crabs.

I will water ski in my box across the
Windy, wild waves of the Pacific Ocean,
Then crash-land in the jungle,
The colour of grass.

Daniel Ashford (8)
Thurston CE (VC) Primary School, Bury St Edmunds

The Magic Box

(Based on 'Magic Box' by Kit Wright)

I will put in my box . . .
The rustle of paper flying in the wind.

I will put in my box . . .
Three green soldiers speaking in Australian,
The last person on Earth
And the first fish in the salty sea.

I will put in my box . . .
A third arm
And a monkey on a skateboard.

My box is built from canvas and rope and leaves,
With soldiers on the lid and guns in the corners.
Its hinges are the joints of King Kong.

I will scuba dive in my box
Under the warm waters of Niagara Falls,
Then wash up on the coast of Disneyland, Paris.

Joseph Bradley (8)
Thurston CE (VC) Primary School, Bury St Edmunds

The Magic Box

(Based on 'Magic Box' by Kit Wright)

I will put in my box . . .
The dance of the doofus demons.

I will put in my box . . .
Three ginger armies screeching in Japanese,
The last stand where I met the Grim Reaper
And the first dinosaur ever to walk the Earth.

I will put in my box . . .
A tenth planet and a turquoise giraffe
And a cowboy on a panther.

My box is constructed from crystals and diamonds and bones,
With yeti teeth on the lid and toffees in the corners.
Its hinges are the legs of a frog.

I will sail in my box across the black sea on a stormy night
And arrive at a Hawaiian beach where it is warm
And the sand is warm.

Cameron Cunningham (8)
Thurston CE (VC) Primary School, Bury St Edmunds

The Magic Box

(Based on 'Magic Box' by Kit Wright)

I will put in my box . . .
The sweet sound of singing swallows.

I will put in my box . . .
Three shiny, smiley, silver suns screaming in Slovakian,
The last super citrus from a citrus tree
And the first sound of a slapping seal.

I will put in my box . . .
A third gill of a fish,
A carrot on a tree and an apple in the ground.

My box is designed from stars and pearls and crystals,
With Christmas trees on the lid and icicles in the corners.
Its hinges are the kneecaps of dragonflies.

I will dive in my box over the stormy Asian ocean
Then arrive at a tropical island in Hollywood,
The colour of aqua.

Megan Holland (8)
Thurston CE (VC) Primary School, Bury St Edmunds

The Magic Box

(Based on 'Magic Box' by Kit Wright)

I will put in my box . . .
The sound of a football bursting on a wet, windy
Wednesday morning.

I will put in my box . . .
Three tan teddy bears told in Spanish,
The last bone of an ancient mummy
And the first slice of yellow butter.

I will put in my box . . .
The sixty-first minute and a red sea,
A man on a lily pad and a frog in a house.

I will waterski in my box
On the warm, calm Caribbean Sea,
Then arrive at a rainforest in Cuba,
The colour of green trees.

Maddie Parsons (8)
Thurston CE (VC) Primary School, Bury St Edmunds

The Magic Box

(Based on 'Magic Box' by Kit Wright)

I will put in my box . . .
The *grrr* of a lion
And the sound of a rock crashing down a mountain.

I will put in my box . . .
A three-headed person and a red sky
And the last bullet of the day
And the first born chipmunk.

My box is fashioned from gold and crystals and stone,
With a skeleton on the lid and chocolate in the corners.
Its hinges are the jawbones of a cobra.

I will kite-surf in my box
On the high raging waves of the pirate's sea,
Then arrive at Florida,
The colour of silver.

Josh Deeks (8)
Thurston CE (VC) Primary School, Bury St Edmunds

The Magic Box

(Based on 'Magic Box' by Kit Wright)

I will put in my box . . .
Three diamond football matches
Shouted in Mexican,
The last day of the war and the first born chipmunk.

I will put in my box . . .
A tenth planet and a turquoise giraffe
And an elephant on a turtle.

My box is crafted from diamonds, rubies and crystals,
With a ghost on the lid and bananas in the corners.
Its hinges are the jaws of a cobra.

I will sail in my box
Across the Pacific Ocean in the wind
And sail ashore at the luxurious Cromer beach.

Steven Quercia-Smale (8)
Thurston CE (VC) Primary School, Bury St Edmunds

Young Writers Information

We hope you have enjoyed reading this book - and that you will continue to enjoy it in the coming years.

If you like reading and writing poetry drop us a line, or give us a call, and we'll send you a free information pack.

Alternatively if you would like to order further copies of this book or any of our other titles, then please give us a call or log onto our website at www.youngwriters.co.uk.

Young Writers Information
Remus House
Coltsfoot Drive
Peterborough
PE2 9JX
(01733) 890066